Contents

Cumberland's Haig Colliery was perched on a clifftop near Whitehaven and in this 1972 scene, its yard is being shunted by Barclay saddle tank *King*. Haig survived demolition after its 1986 closure but was shut down as a museum at the end of 2015. GORDON EDGAR

EDITOR AND AUTHOR: Nick Pigott

PRODUCTION EDITOR: Pauline Hawkins

DESIGNER: Sean Phillips, Atg-Media.com

COVER DESIGN: Holly Munro

REPROGRAPHICS: Jonathan Schofield and Paul Fincham

PUBLISHER: Steve O'Hara

PUBLISHING DIRECTOR: Dan Savage

COMMERCIAL DIRECTOR: Nigel Hole

MARKETING MANAGER: Charlotte Park cpark@mortons.co.uk

DISTRIBUTION EXECUTIVE: John Sharratt tradesales@mortons.co.uk classicmagazines.co.uk/tradesales

PRINTED BY: William Gibbons & Sons, Wolverhampton

ISBN: 978-1-909128668

PUBLISHED BY: Mortons Media Group Ltd, Media Centre, Morton Way, Horncastle, Lincolnshire LN9 6JR Tel: 01507 529529

© Copyright Mortons Media Group Ltd, 2016 All Rights Reserved.

MORTONS
MEDIA GROUP LTD

FRONT COVER: Main image: King Coal's golden crown is no more. The long reign of the deep mine in Britain came to an end in 2015 after more than three centuries and now all the nation is left with are memories. This crown, inlaid with a red diamond, adorned the upcast shaft at Thoresby Colliery, one of the last three deep mines to close last year. Left inset: Putting a brave face on it... members of the very last shift at the very last colliery pose for the national media at Kellingley after coming up to the surface for the final time on December 18, 2015. PRESS ASSOCIATION Right inset: Diamonds, albeit black ones, also featured on the sides of locomotives allocated to British Rail's coal sector in the 1980s and early' 90s. This is No. 58004 at Bentinck Colliery in January 1994. RAIL PHOTOPRINTS

A LONG AND GI

THE year 2016 will be remembered as one of the most significant in the annals of industrial history, for it is the first for more than three centuries in which no deep-mined coal has been produced in Great Britain.

That such a state of affairs could come to pass in the nation that gave birth to the Industrial Revolution is extraordinary and serves to underline the monumental social changes that have taken place in the UK in recent years.

For hundreds of years, 'King Coal' reigned supreme, reaching a pinnacle almost exactly a century ago and remaining one of Britain's greatest industries until the mid-1980s.

Yet today there are millions of youngsters who've never set eyes on a piece of coal in their lives and who wonder why they see so many "big wheels planted in the grass" when they travel through certain parts of Britain.

Those wheels are, of course, the pulley sheaves that once sat proudly atop the winding towers, spinning day and night to send men deep into the bowels of the earth to bring up the 'black diamonds' that fuelled the heavy industries of the 19th and 20th centuries. Today, either whole or cut in half, they sit in roadside memorial gardens in former mining communities... and are sadly often the only visible evidence that a colliery ever stood on the site.

It is difficult to convey to anyone who never experienced it just how vast the British coal industry was at its peak. Just one large mine and its attendant housing and tips could cover an area the size of a whole village, providing a living for as many as 3,000 men and their families. A mile or so down the road there would be another pit, then another, then another... and so it would go on right through the valley or coalfield – and that was just on the surface; below the ground, the mines were even more extensive, their labyrinthine networks often spreading as far as six or seven miles from the colliery buildings.

An impression of the size of the industry as a whole can be gained from the fact that there were more than 900 such collieries in the coalfields of Britain when the present Queen came to the throne, and at the height of the British empire in the late Victorian era there were three times that many.

Those were the days when Great Britain – with an area less than

Thumbs up! When this photo was taken in 1979, the coal industry was in a powerful position as a major component of British society. PRESS ASSOCIATION

From Delight To Despair: W

- In 1913 – the high point of the British coal mining industry in terms of size and productivity – there were 3,024 mines employing 1.1million miners producing 287million tons of coal a year.

- In 1947, the first year of nationalisation, there were 1,296 mines and 707,000 men producing 187m tons a year.

1/500th of the world's surface area – produced almost *half* the planet's mineral tonnage! Small wonder that the empire's industrial might is said to have been built on a foundation of coal and steel.

In those days, it would have been utterly unthinkable for it all to have vanished little more than a

century later, but the demise of deep coal mining in the UK occurred on December 18, 2015 when the final shift ended at Kellingley Colliery in North Yorkshire.

The closure of that famous pit brought to an end an aspect of the industry so old that its genesis is impossible to accurately pinpoint but

Heads down! By the end of 2015, the last handful of British miners had just lost their jobs and the nation that gave birth to the Industrial Revolution no longer possessed a single working deep colliery.

ABOVE: A stark reminder of past glories: Plinthed headstock pulley wheels in former mining communities, such as this one near Coalville, Leicestershire, are now often the only signs that a colliery ever stood in the vicinity. NICK PIGOTT

ABOVE: There have been many highlights along the way. Mechanisation in the second half of the 20th century brought massive advances in productivity and efficiency and barely a week went by without a workforce somewhere in the country being able to proudly pose for a portrait such as this at Calverton Colliery in 1992. Less than a week later came the shock news that this and 30 other pits were to close, but Calverton's profitability was such that it was taken over by a private company, RJB Mining, and remained open for a further seven years.

a Difference a Century Makes!

- In the strike year of 1984, there were 165 pits and 140,000 men.

- In 1994, the year the industry was privatised, there were 20 mines and 18,000 men producing 30m tons

- In 2016 there are no deep coal mines at all!

which is generally considered to date from the early 1700s. Coal mining itself had been going on for many hundreds of years before that, of course, as explained on the following pages, and some of the hand-dug bellpits had extended 100ft or more into the ground in dry areas, but they didn't qualify as deep mines in the accepted sense that

later saw men working at well over 20 times that depth.

The invention of water-pumping engines in the early 18th century made it possible to penetrate further into the earth's crust than had been possible with bellpits, but it wasn't until the first half of the 19th century that mines began to really grow in size.

The final transition to the immense modern colliery complexes of the 20th century commenced just over a hundred years ago when it became a legal requirement to equip new mines with winding towers built of steel instead of timber.

Those towers, better known as headstocks or headgear, were the most visible surface aspects of any pit - tall structures of steel or concrete often visible for miles around and forming a focal point for their community. Each tower was a symbol of industrial ▶

might, each mine a hive of activity, each community a source of pride.

Mining was one of the toughest jobs a man could do and the hardships were many, especially in the years prior to creation of the National Coal Board in 1947, yet most ex-miners say they wouldn't have wanted to do anything else. They had a love-hate relationship with their work, often claiming not to enjoy it... yet demonstrating a fierce pride and loyalty to their profession if ever it was threatened.

The passionate reactions of the Kellingley workers as they were interviewed by the media on their final day demonstrated heartbreak and anger in far greater measure than is usually the case in less demanding industries... and not simply because they were losing their jobs. In fact, so far did the emotions overflow as the men came to the surface for the last time that BBC Radio had to issue a public apology for expletives contained in a live news interview.

Most men have a soft spot for their former workplaces and are always saddened when they see how a productive and often profitable hive of industry has been flattened and replaced by a warehouse, wine bar, wind farm or wasteland. This deep-seated fondness is borne out by the fact that a retired collier's home will usually have a brightly polished safety lamp in pride of place on the lounge mantelpiece or sideboard.

In their working days, miners looked out for one another when underground - it was often the only way to survive in the hazardous conditions. As a result, strong bonds of friendship were formed between the men and their families and that led in turn to an unshakable sense of community and pride that survives to this day.

Something that doesn't readily occur to members of the public is that a coalface worker went every day where no human being had ever been before! Many people now fear that the UK itself has taken an alarmingly large step into the unknown by depriving itself of its deep-mining ability.

Old King Coal's death has been a protracted one, but the crown was finally knocked off by cheap imports and climate change fears. This was not an industry that died a natural death, superseded by technological advance. On the contrary, the UK still consumes tens of millions of tonnes of coal a year and will do so for the next few years at least. The difference is that today's supplies are either dug from opencast mines or purchased from abroad, much of it from countries with inferior working conditions and far poorer safety records than the UK.

Fossil fuels are therefore still being burned in Britain, resulting in marginal environmental benefit to the atmosphere despite the nation's sacrifice of its deep collieries. On top of that, some nations are still building deep mines and erecting coal-fired power stations despite the global environmental pressures that have forced the UK to abandon such a huge natural asset.

Half a dozen or so minuscule drift mines continue in Britain with a mere two or three workers each, and two larger drift mines in the Welsh anthracite field are currently 'mothballed' on a care-and-maintenance basis, but the death of the tin, fluorspar and lead-mining industries decades ago means that only a few potash and gypsum plants continue the proud tradition of deep mining in the UK. Of the near 1,000 collieries that came into

ABOVE: The close relationship between coal and power generation was established many decades ago and did much to prolong the longevity of the mining industry. With the cooling towers of Drakelow power station prominent in the background, RSH 0-6-0 saddle tank No. 1848 *Progress* shunts at Cadley Hill Colliery on June 19, 1976. BRIAN SHARPE

ABOVE: Looking at the ancient wooden wagons, few people would guess that this evocative scene was captured as relatively recently as the mid-1980s. The location was Ashington Colliery, in Northumberland, and the National Coal Board's ex-British Rail diesel-hydraulic locomotive No. D9500 was passing classmate D9521 as it arrived with loaded wagons from nearby Lynemouth Colliery on March 25, 1986. GORDON EDGAR

INSERT RIGHT: How the Ashington scene looks today: a slick new 'business park' with landscaped gardens and ornamental fountains.

public ownership in 1947, there are no operational examples left at all.

Almost all have been demolished, leaving only a couple of derelict ones plus a handful that have been turned into museums.

As Britain was the largest producer of coal in the world little more than a century ago, the complete destruction of the colliery network has taken place within a single human lifetime. A sobering thought.

Notwithstanding current carbon legislation, the policy of filling shafts with concrete and demolishing surface buildings instead of mothballing some of the more productive pits in case of future national emergencies has been criticised in some quarters as dangerously short-sighted.

Whatever your view, there's no doubt that it's an extremely sad end for the industry that fired the Industrial Revolution and helped put the 'Great' into Britain.

The story of how one of the nation's greatest industries was gained and

ABOVE: In their heyday, colliery yards could be large and as busy as those of similar size on the main line rail network. This was the scene at Lady Victoria Colliery, at Newtongrange, south of Edinburgh, in 1966. NATIONAL ARCHIVE

ABOVE: Pillars of the community: The 200ft headstocks of Clipstone Colliery were the tallest steel-built ones in the country and still stand, although the majority of the buildings around them have been demolished. They were of the ground-mounted Koepe friction type and this photo demonstrates the difference between upcast and downcast shafts. The upcast on the right has the centre of its tower encased in shuttering to help control the flow of ventilation air through the underground workings (further details on pages 54 and 89). ROBIN STEWART-SMITH

RIGHT: The author 2,267ft (691 metres) below ground at Thoresby Colliery a few weeks before its closure in 2015. Thoresby was one of the most productive pits in Britain and, as our front cover image shows, was proud to proclaim itself the 'jewel in the crown' of the East Midlands coalfield. As was the case with many British mines in recent times, it closed despite possessing substantial reserves of coal.

then lost is a fascinating one and this souvenir bookazine sets out to record its history for posterity and pay tribute to mining, mines and miners.

My own association with collieries began in the late-1960s and I was fortunate to visit several in their operational days, including Thoresby, Littleton, Bolsover, Rossington, Ashington, Maerdy, Snowdown, Asfordby and Kellingley. My last underground visit took place at Thoresby before its closure last year.

So large and varied was the industry that it's almost impossible to generalise when reporting on it, for there was at least one exception to virtually every rule and every situation. It also has to be said that history books and reference sources contain often-conflicting information and varying statistics, particularly where 'first', 'last', 'largest' and so on are concerned. This publication is therefore an attempt to iron out some of the imperfections and present a general overview that will hopefully appeal to ex-miners and their families as well as to those who simply have an admiration for the skills and history associated with collieries and coal mining.

Readers are asked to bear in mind that the terminology used in the pits has varied over the years, not only from area to area but also from era to era. What was known commonly as a tub, for example, can be a tram, a dram, a hutch or a mine car, depending on which location and which timeframe is being referred to. Hundreds of years ago, a 'pit' was, strictly speaking, another word for a shaft, but in common usage it has come to be known as a general term for a colliery and is used as an alternative to mine or colliery in this publication. By the same token, operating practices also differed; the way things were done at a certain colliery in Wales in the 19th century may not have been the way they were done in Yorkshire or Scotland in the 20th, and so on.

I have attempted to steer a neutral line where politics and union affairs are concerned and to present both sides of an argument or simply state plain facts, but if it is felt I have inadvertently deviated from this line at any point, I apologise. As this publication is primarily to mark the end of the deep-mining industry, I have also opted to use the past tense in many chapters even though some of the practices and machines described continue to be used in other parts of the world.

Every precaution has been taken to ensure accuracy, but any errors are mine and mine alone. It's inevitable with a subject as vast and varied as coal mining that readers will have comments and observations of their own, so if you feel you can add or amend anything, I would be delighted to hear from you. You can email me at: nickpigott@icloud.com or write to me care of the publishers (address on page 3).

Finally, many thanks to the miners and senior mining engineers who helped with this project and to my wife Suzanne for 'bearing with me' while I burned the midnight oil – or should that be coal!

I hope this souvenir serves as a record of a great and sadly missed industry.　　　　NICK PIGOTT

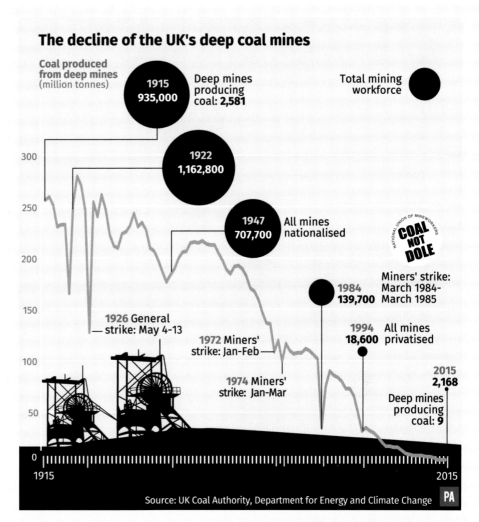

ABOVE: This graphic charts the decline of the UK coal industry between 1915 – when there were more than 2,500 deep mines – and a century later, when there were none. Significant landmarks in the history of the industry are shown, such as nationalisation, privatisation and the major industrial disputes.

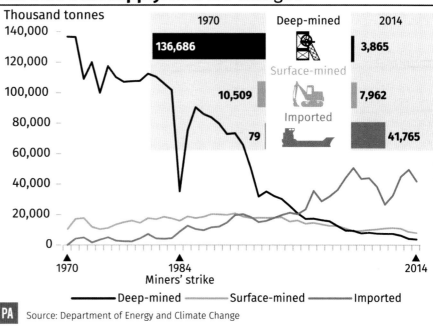

ABOVE: This graphic shows how imported coal has overtaken the indigenous deep-mined product, the crucial point occurring at about the turn of the present century. The supply of surface-mined (opencast) coal has remained pretty constant for the past 30 years.

'BURIED SUNSHINE'
HOW COAL WAS FORMED

THREE hundred million years ago, the area on which Britain now stands was a vast shallow tropical estuary into which great rivers flowed into the sea and deposited sand, mud and silt. The continents we know today had not yet formed and were constantly changing shape as violent upheavals took place in the earth's crust.

Every few million years, these changes would reduce the depth of water covering the land and create hot swampy conditions in which primitive ferns and trees could grow. Over thousands of years, these forests grew and died, forming a thick layer of decaying matter in the swamps and lagoons as they did so, until another change in the shape of the land allowed the sea level to rise and water to flow over the area, depositing layer upon layer of mud and sand and burying the rotting vegetable matter.

As the water slowly subsided in these river deltas, as it did frequently during the earth's formative stages, the level of silt and clay gradually built up until there was sufficient depth for plants and trees to start growing again. Meanwhile, the previous layers of vegetable matter underneath were gradually being turned by pressure and heat into peat (a soft brown spongy substance) and the layers of sediment were being solidified into rock under the tons of weight above them.

This cycle of growth, decay, flooding, sediment cover and re-growth was repeated scores of times over the course of the prehistoric Carboniferous Period, which ran from approximately 360million years BC to 298million years BC, and each cycle formed a new layer of decomposed vegetation and a new layer of mud and sand. As each new deposit was laid down, the ever-increasing weight further compressed the older seams below, turning the peat into lignite and finally into coal.

To give an idea of the rate of compression, a 30ft depth of peat would take about 10,000 years to compress into 5ft of lignite (a form of soft brown coal), which in turn would compress over many more millennia into 3ft of hard, black bituminous coal.

This explains why coal is found in layers, for each seam represents one of the cycles mentioned above and the depth of each seam reveals roughly how long each cycle lasted. It also helps explain why coal burns, for the energy contained within it is energy from the sun that was absorbed by the trees and plants and trapped underground ever since. It is released when the coal is burned and gives rise to one of the affectionate nicknames coal has gained over the years – 'Buried Sunshine'.

Other names include 'Black Diamonds' and 'Black Gold', although the latter is more commonly associated with oil.

The measures found in Britain were laid down during the Carboniferous Period (i.e. between 360m and 298m years ago) and the stratified rocks normally comprise shale, sandstone, mudstone and fireclay as well as coal. It is a common error among members of the public to confuse coal seams with coal measures. The latter include the interleaved layers of rock and there can be as many as 100 seams within the measures, although most are only an inch or so thick and not worth mining.

Anything above 2ft is commercially exploitable and in parts of Warwickshire and Staffordshire, the seams can be as thick as 30ft. Most measures in the UK contain anything up to 30 seams ranging from eight inches to 10ft. Seams thinner than 2ft were sometimes mined in conjunction with other minerals such as ironstone or fireclay.

Every seam in Britain is identified by a name and those which ran for many miles, such as the Barnsley 'Top Hard', would be tapped by several different collieries. A fair proportion of the titles were based on local nicknames and if all the thin seams are taken into

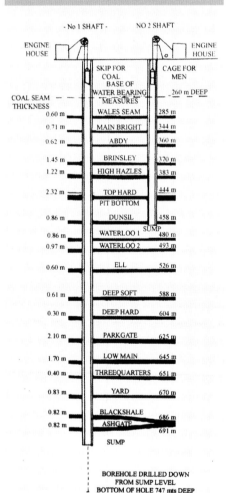

BILSTHORPE COLLIERY
- SHAFT SECTION -
NOT TO SCALE

COAL SEAM THICKNESS		
	WALES SEAM	285 m
0.60 m		
0.71 m	MAIN BRIGHT	344 m
0.62 m	ABDY	360 m
1.45 m	BRINSLEY	370 m
1.22 m	HIGH HAZLES	383 m
2.32 m	TOP HARD	444 m
	PIT BOTTOM	
0.86 m	DUNSIL	458 m
0.86 m	WATERLOO 1	480 m
0.97 m	WATERLOO 2	493 m
0.60 m	ELL	526 m
0.61 m	DEEP SOFT	588 m
0.30 m	DEEP HARD	604 m
2.10 m	PARKGATE	625 m
1.70 m	LOW MAIN	645 m
0.40 m	THREEQUARTERS	651 m
0.83 m	YARD	670 m
0.82 m	BLACKSHALE	686 m
0.82 m	ASHGATE	691 m
	SUMP	

BOREHOLE DRILLED DOWN FROM SUMP LEVEL
BOTTOM OF HOLE 747 mts DEEP

ABOVE: Eighteen seams! A cross-section of the shafts at Bilsthorpe Colliery showing the names, depths and thicknesses of the seams they passed through. At this particular mine, one of the vertical shafts extended only as far as the Top Hard, drifts at gradients of between 1-in-6 and 1-in-4 continuing from there to access the Parkgate, Low Main and Blackshale seams.

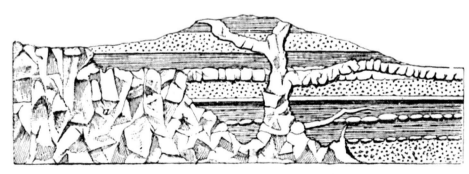

ABOVE: The effect of volcanic activity on coal measures can be dramatic, as seen in this diagram. The larva that forced its way through the ground millions of years ago has solidified to form igneous rocks, some of which mimic sedimentary rocks by running parallel to the coal seams.

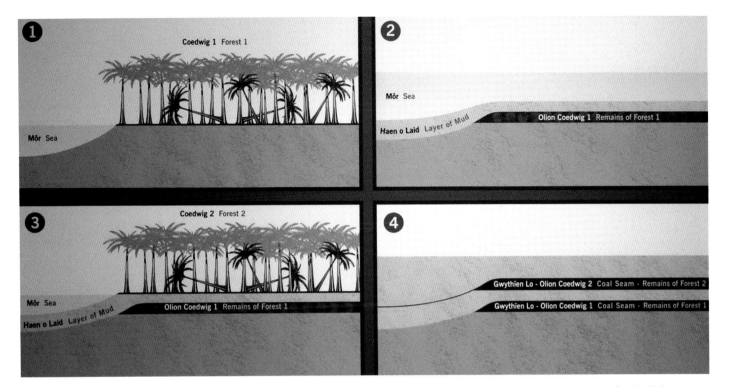

ABOVE: How coal seams were laid down: This bi-lingual diagram on display at the Big Pit mining museum in Blaenafon, South Wales, shows how a prehistoric forest died and became covered by sea and mud, followed by a second forest once the water subsided, forming a second layer, which in turn became covered in mud, sand, silt and clay. Those substances eventually hardened into rocks and the process was repeated many times during the 62million-year Carboniferous Period.

account, there were several hundred in the UK as a whole.

Carboniferous means 'coal-bearing' and the 62million-year lifespan of that period coincided with primitive animal life on Earth. In fact, fossils of tiny invertebrates are sometimes found alongside fossilised leaves in the shale next to the coal.

Coal lies in 'basins', a reference to the swamps in which it was formed, and there are five primary basins beneath the mainland of Britain containing a total of about 50 accessible coalfields if all the smallest ones are included.

When the measures were first laid down, they were reasonably level, but towards the end of the Carboniferous Period, colossal earth movements began to develop, forcing the land containing the seams into undulating folds known as anticlines and synclines (the hills and valleys we know today). Over millions of years, seams that had ended up on top of anticlines were worn away through the erosive action of frost, ice, wind, rain and rivers, which explains why there is no coal on top of the Pennines, for example.

Other seams fell victim to massive faults and fractures in the earth that broke their continuity, so that they appeared to stop abruptly but in fact continued at different heights or depths. Washouts of seams in certain locations posed similar problems for miners.

The thickest seams lie at about 10,000ft (too deep to be economically mined by conventional means), but most are found between 500 and 2,000ft with many much closer to the surface than that.

Coal measures overlaid by more recently formed sedimentary rocks, such as those laid down in the Jurassic and Triassic Periods, are known as concealed coalfields, while those that appear close to the surface are referred to as 'exposed', even though they may be covered by layers of soil and sub-soil and are only literally exposed at the edges of the basins or in places where natural erosion has taken place.

The commonest type of coal found in Britain is bituminous, which splits easily along its cleats and can be cleaved by hand-held picks fairly easily. The western half of the South Wales coalfield and a few areas in central Scotland contain rich deposits of anthracite, the highest-ranking grade of coal in terms of carbon content. Anthracite was formed millions of years ago as a result of volcanic larva intruding into bituminous deposits, the intense heat altering the properties of the coal. As can be seen in the diagram on page 10, these so-called igneous rocks can even end up lying parallel to the coal seams.

In the world as a whole, coalfields are located in more than 70 countries on every continent (including Antarctica), with the largest being in Russia, and it is estimated that there are still more than 850billion tonnes of accessible coal reserves worldwide. ● ▶

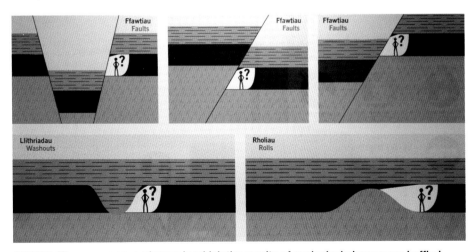

ABOVE: There were several ways in which the results of geological phenomena baffled early miners and five of them are illustrated at the Big Pit museum. In each case, the green and orange levels represent rocks with the black coal seam falling or rising in relation to them, depending on the type of fault. A washout usually occurred when a subterranean river removed a portion of coal that had been lying in its path, while a roll would be caused by the forcing-up of rock by natural movement of the earth.

TYPES OF COAL

Anthracite coal

Parrot or Cannel coal
Dull, hard coal without layers.

Bituminous coal
Made up of layers, can be bright and glossy or dull and sooty

ABOVE: To the untrained eye, most coal looks the same but there are numerous types, three of which are shown in this Scottish Mining Museum exhibit. The most common is bituminous (right), which in the case of this exhibit is bright, glossy and layered. The parrot, or cannel, on the left is dull and hard, not unlike shale at first glance, while the anthracite at the top is shiny and hard with few signs of layers.

ANTHRACITE: A hard, shiny coal with few impurities, a very high fixed carbon content of at least 93% and the highest calorific value of all true coals. Sometimes known as stone coal, it burns with great heat, little smoke and minimum ash. It is the most mature type of coal and is good for steel making, gas generation and domestic use.

SEMI-ANTHRACITE: Also known as steam coal, this burns more readily than pure anthracite and, as the name denotes, is mainly used for the production of steam in locomotive and other boilers. Its carbon content is 83-93% and it gives off very little smoke when burning.

SEMI-BITUMINOUS: A cross between semi-anthracite and the normal bituminous variety, with a carbon content of 73 to 83%.

BITUMINOUS: This is the common pit coal and is so called because it contains a hydro-carbon substance called bitumen. Good for household and industrial use but can be smoky. Carbon content 47 to 73%.

SUB-BITUMINOUS (also known as steam coal or black lignite): used for locomotive and ship boilers. Shares with bituminous a carbon content of 47 to 73%.

CANNEL: Burns with a bright flame like a candle (hence its similar name) and crackles when burning. Sometimes known by the nickname 'parrot'. Carbon content: 35 to 47%.

LIGNITE: The lowest rank of coal due to its relatively low heat content. It is much younger than fully formed coal and the process of conversion from wood to coal is incomplete. Formed from partly compressed peat (see below), it is reasonably soft and certain inferior forms of it are sometimes known as 'brown coal'. It contains 30 to 55% carbon.

PEAT: A soft combustible vegetable matter occurring at the surface that is compacted and partly carbonised (as much as 50% in some cases) but which has not yet had time to be compressed by the earth into true coal.

In addition to the above, there is **graphite**, which is 99% fixed carbon and as such almost impossible to ignite. Although it is officially a member of the coal family, it is not mined for the same purposes as the other types.

(Coke is the lightweight solid material left after the gases have been extracted from coal by baking or 'cooking' in an oven. It has a high carbon content and few impurities.)

Typical of the South Wales coalfield was the small town of Mountain Ash, whose colliery nestled in the narrow Cynon Valley. This view from October 1972 shows Robert Stephenson & Hawthorn-built saddle tank No. 7139 shunting the pit's busy yard. ROGER SIVITER/COLOUR-RAIL

WHERE COAL IS FOUND

BRITAIN is often described as an 'island of coal', but only certain areas are classed as coalfields. The largest ones are basically to be found in South Wales, the East and West Midlands, West and South Yorkshire, Lancashire, the North East and central Scotland.

The reason for the specific and highly localised nature of the boundaries shown on the map on the next page is that the fields represent only the relatively exposed and accessible parts of the coal measures. In many locations, deposits of coal extend further afield but are concealed beneath millions of tons of younger rocks. This explains, for example, why Lincolnshire is not considered a coalfield even though deposits are known to exist at great depth beneath it all the way from the Nottinghamshire border to the North Sea coast.

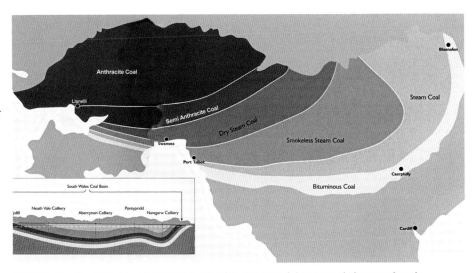

ABOVE: The South Wales coalfield is a complex one containing several classes of coal – bituminous in the east, grades of steam coal in the centre and anthracite in the west. See over for a general map of the UK's coalfields. ▶

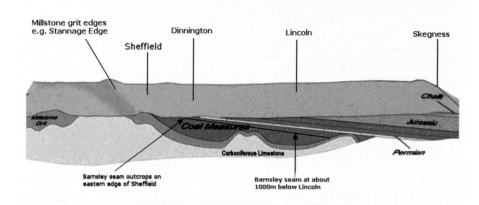

Labels on diagram: Millstone grit edges e.g. Stannage Edge · Sheffield · Dinnington · Lincoln · Skegness · Chalk · Coal Measures · Jurassic · Carboniferous Limestone · Permian · Barnsley seam outcrops on eastern edge of Sheffield · Barnsley seam at about 1000m below Lincoln

Coal less than 1,200m below surface (brown)

Coal more than 1,200m below surface (green)

Coalfields fall into two main categories – exposed and concealed. The latter usually lie below more recently laid rock strata and the diagram on the left shows how the Nottinghamshire coalfield extends at great depth all the way under Lincolnshire and far out into the North Sea. In Victorian times, boreholes were dug in Lincolnshire to ascertain the depth and this Woodhall Spa road sign contains a somewhat incongruous winding tower image as a reminder of those days.

The land that now constitutes the British mainland was once largely covered in coal measures (apart from areas such as central Wales and the Scottish Highlands, which had been covered by solid land rather than swamps in prehistoric times), but, as explained in the previous chapter, earth upheavals and subsequent erosion mean that only certain areas are classified as coalfields.

The region generally considered to be the principal mining district, even though it's not the largest, is the South Wales coalfield. This extends almost 90 miles east to west across the bulk of the famous 'mountains and valleys' region of Glamorgan and Monmouthshire and although only 16 miles across at its widest point, covers some 1,000 square miles and contained more than 600 collieries in its heyday.

In the peak year of 1913, almost 20% of **South Wales** coal was being exported through Barry or Cardiff docks and the two together accounted for the largest coal-exporting port complex in the world at the time. In 1851, there had been 951 people living in the Rhondda valley; by 1924, there were 167,000! The last deep mine in the Valleys was Tower Colliery, which closed for the second and last time in 2008.

The western portion of the coalfield contains large deposits of high-quality anthracite but there was a smaller and less productive anthracite field, known as the Daucleddau, further west in **Pembrokeshire**, which was effectively part of the same field but separated by Carmarthen Bay. The Pembrokeshire seams were mostly thin, plagued by fault lines and the best anthracite could only be found at considerable depth. That field's last mine closed at the end of the 1940s.

The **North Wales** coalfield is 45 miles long from north to south but less than 10 miles wide. Its exposed area stretches from the Irish Sea coast down to Oswestry, in Shropshire, but to the east the deposits extend beneath a covering of newer strata and are continuous underground with the Lancashire and Staffordshire measures. It is sometimes considered two coalfields - the Flintshire and the Denbighshire.

Although its seams were heavily faulted, North Wales contained one of the largest and most prolific collieries in Wales - Llay Main, near Wrexham, which as early as 1929 broke into the 'millionaires club' with an output of 1,057,592 tons. The region also possessed one of the principality's last operational collieries, Point of Ayr, which didn't close until 1996. There is also a tiny and little-known detached coalfield on the island of Anglesey, but mining there ceased in the 1880s.

On the eastern side of the River Severn can be found the **Somerset & Gloucestershire** coalfield. The main part of this is about 25 miles long and it runs roughly through the gap between Bristol and Bath, extending down to Radstock. It is believed to be an extension of the South Wales coalfield but its seams were generally thinner. Coal is first recorded as being mined there in 1223 and the last colliery, Kilmersdon, closed in 1973.

Although part of Gloucestershire, the **Forest of Dean** is thought of as a coalfield in its own right. It lies on the western bank of the River Severn roughly between Cinderford and Coleford and, although only 34 square miles in area, is one of the oldest in Britain, having been worked in Roman times. It is also one of the best known by virtue of the Forest Free Miners (see panel on p119).

Moving north, we come to the various coalfields of the West Midlands. The largest of these is the **North Staffordshire**, most of which is taken up by the Potteries field, whose 100 square miles contained some of Britain's largest collieries. There are more than 30 workable seams, making a total

ABOVE: One of the smaller British coalfields lies in Somerset but its mines are long-closed. On July 9, 1965, British Railways diesel-hydraulic locomotive No. D7046 passes the spoil heap and engine shed of Old Mills Colliery as it gets away from Midsomer Norton with loaded coal wagons from Radstock to Bristol East Depot. DEREK FEAR/RAIL PHTOTOPRINTS

The Coalfields of Britain

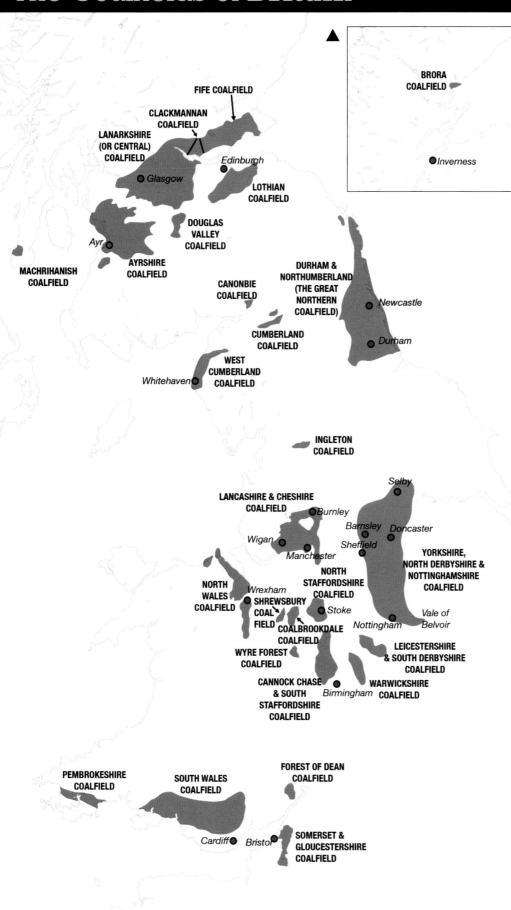

Note: Some fields were sub-divided into smaller sections with their own names, e.g. the Burnley field, the Dudley field. The Somerset & Gloucestershire was sometimes known as the Bristol & Somerset. Some very minor fields are not marked but are mentioned in the text. Also not shown are concealed coalfields, such as those under Lincolnshire and Oxfordshire.

BRORA COALFIELD

Inverness

FIFE COALFIELD

CLACKMANNAN COALFIELD

LANARKSHIRE (OR CENTRAL) COALFIELD

Edinburgh

Glasgow

LOTHIAN COALFIELD

DOUGLAS VALLEY COALFIELD

Ayr

AYRSHIRE COALFIELD

MACHRIHANISH COALFIELD

CANONBIE COALFIELD

DURHAM & NORTHUMBERLAND (THE GREAT NORTHERN COALFIELD)

Newcastle

CUMBERLAND COALFIELD

Durham

WEST CUMBERLAND COALFIELD

Whitehaven

INGLETON COALFIELD

Selby

LANCASHIRE & CHESHIRE COALFIELD

Burnley

Barnsley

Doncaster

Wigan

Sheffield

Manchester

YORKSHIRE, NORTH DERBYSHIRE & NOTTINGHAMSHIRE COALFIELD

NORTH STAFFORDSHIRE COALFIELD

NORTH WALES COALFIELD

Wrexham

SHREWSBURY COAL FIELD

Stoke

COALBROOKDALE COALFIELD

Nottingham

Vale of Belvoir

WYRE FOREST COALFIELD

LEICESTERSHIRE & SOUTH DERBYSHIRE COALFIELD

CANNOCK CHASE & SOUTH STAFFORDSHIRE COALFIELD

Birmingham

WARWICKSHIRE COALFIELD

PEMBROKESHIRE COALFIELD

SOUTH WALES COALFIELD

FOREST OF DEAN COALFIELD

Cardiff

Bristol

SOMERSET & GLOUCESTERSHIRE COALFIELD

KENT COALFIELD

Dover

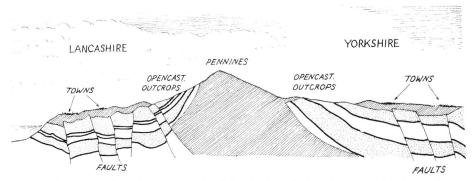

ABOVE: A cross-section of northern England showing how the Pennine hills divide the coal measures on either side. Note the extensive amount of faulting, especially in Lancashire.

ABOVE: An indication of how crowded the coalfields were in the early years of mining can be gained from this engraving from the late 18th century. There are three mines within very close proximity, each with its own timber headgear, the latter by then already starting to resemble the huge structures they would become over the next century and a half. The atmospheric steam engine in this portrait is an example of the Newcomen design.

thickness of almost 150ft, more than anywhere else in the UK, but some are so faulted as to be almost vertical (so-called 'rearer' workings).

The **South Staffordshire**, or Dudley coalfield as it is sometimes known, covered an area of about 80 square miles extending from Wolverhampton down into north Worcestershire. It was renowned for its 'Ten Yard Coal', a seam approaching 30ft in thickness that was actually a dozen thin seams overlying each other with no intermediate layers of dirt or rock. This lay at less than 400ft below the surface in some places and no other part of Britain had so much coal available at such a shallow depth. A number of South Staffordshire's mines flooded due to lack of maintenance during the 1921 miners' strike and never reopened, but Baggeridge - the last colliery in the 'Black Country' - survived until 1968.

Immediately north of this field was the **Cannock Chase** coalfield, which was effectively separated from it by a major geological division known as the Bentley Fault. Cannock Chase contained Littleton Colliery, which continued in production until 1993, and Lea Hall, which in 1960 had been one of the NCB's all-new showcase mines.

Some of the thickest seams in Britain, ranging from 7ft to 23ft, were to be found in the **Warwickshire** coalfield. This lay in the Coventry, Warwick, Nuneaton and Tamworth area and it is an indication of how prodigious it was that Daw Mill Colliery, eight miles north-west of Coventry, was expected to be the last operational mine left in Britain until a major underground fire caused its unexpected closure in 2013.

The county of Shropshire has three coalfields - the **Shrewsbury, Coalbrookdale** and **Wyre Forest**. Of these, Coalbrookdale (also known as the Shropshire field) is the largest and considered one of the cradles of the Industrial Revolution thanks to the iron ore smelting developments of Abraham Darby. Although the Wyre Forest field has been a memory since its last mine, Highley, closed in 1969, it retains a link with coal to this day as steam locomotives of the Severn Valley Railway run through Highley en route from Bridgnorth to Kidderminster.

The **Leicestershire** and **South Derbyshire** coalfields lie close to an ancient geological area known as Charnwood Forest and stretch 17 miles from just east of Burton-upon-

Trent to just west of Leicester. They are sometimes thought of as one field, but lie on different sides of a geological dividing point known as the Ashby Anticline.

Each part contains a sizeable mining town - Coalville in Leicestershire and Swadlincote in Derbyshire - and each had about a dozen collieries in NCB days. Records of workings go back to medieval times and evidence of room & pillar working has been uncovered in 21st century opencast operations.

In the 1980s, Asfordby Colliery was built near Melton Mowbray to exploit a hitherto unexploited part of Leicestershire, the **Vale of Belvoir** coalfield, but geological and political problems combined to condemn the project to a short life.

One of the best-known mining areas is the **Lancashire & Cheshire** coalfield, a symbol of England's industrial might in the early 20th century when there were more than 300 collieries there employing 94,000 workers and lifting almost 25million tons of coal a year.

It is divided into three smaller fields - Burnley, South Lancashire and East Manchester - and parts of the area are sometimes further sub-divided, with Oldham, St Helens and Wigan having been credited at some stage with fields named after them. The southern part of the East Manchester is known as the Cheshire coalfield and formed a narrow strip to the east of Stockport.

The Manchester field was the most productive in the county and contained some large collieries, such as Moseley Common, Astley Green and Agecroft, which didn't close until summer 1990. The majority of the **Burnley** field was cut off from the main area and, being in hilly terrain, featured more drift mines than was the case in the rest of the county.

At its peak, the Lancashire field as a whole was a large one with numerous easily accessible seams, but they were mostly thin, with the majority being only 2 to 3ft in height. Several of the workings also had a reputation for wetness and it is said that mines in the Wigan field used to pump four tons of water for every ton of coal. Lancashire's products were mainly bituminous and it was known for high-quality coking and gas-making coals.

Separated from Lancashire by the Pennine mountains is Yorkshire, which forms the northern section of Britain's largest coalfield.

This is known as the **Yorkshire, North Derbyshire and Nottinghamshire** coalfield, but for administrative purposes has usually been divided into its respective counties. Sometimes known as the Midland coalfield, it stretches 60 miles from the Leeds and Huddersfield area to Nottingham, taking in Barnsley, Sheffield, Doncaster and Mansfield, and is significantly larger than the South Wales field. In some parts of it, the coal measures are 5,000ft thick and contain as many as 30 workable seams.

Until the Industrial Revolution and the huge demands the steel-making factories of Sheffield and Rotherham began placing on the mining industry, workings were confined to the exposed coalfield but from the 1920s onwards, new sources of coal had to be found and the collieries thus began migrating eastwards to tap into concealed parts of the measures until the coal descended too far beneath the newer rocks to be commercially viable. As an indication of how low and how far the measures extended, test-boring in 1927 found coal 4,000ft beneath Lincoln Cathedral!

Another test bore further east – at Woodhall – couldn't reach the coal but did discover brine water, which gave the village a major new lease of life as an internationally famed health spa.

In Nottinghamshire in the 1920s, a number of mines were built in a part of Sherwood Forest known as the Dukeries because of the number of stately homes in the area. The NCB established several superpits there and in Yorkshire in the 1950s and 60s to serve new power stations in the Trent and Aire valleys and that eastwards expansion culminated in the creation of an all-new **Selby** coalfield in the early 1980s.

There is a very small isolated field in north-west Yorkshire, at Ingleton, and other limited deposits in the nearby Lune Valley, Askrigg and Alston areas. The North Yorkshire Moors also had small deposits, but all these areas mainly supplied local needs only.

Of more importance from a national standpoint was the **West Cumberland** coalfield, which hugged the Irish Sea coast in the Workington and Whitehaven district. It occupied a narrow strip of land but extended westwards, necessitating under-sea mining from as early as the 18th century. At one point, Whitehaven was one of the most important coal-shipping ports in the country, sending huge tonnages over to Ireland, which had no large coal reserves of its own, mainly only peat and lignite.

By far the oldest and most traditional source of coal in England is the **Durham & Northumberland** field. This is often thought of as two separate entities but geologically is only one, known collectively as the Great Northern Coalfield. It embraces an area of about 800 square miles and runs for 50 miles from Amble in the north to Hartlepool in the south, stretching inland for about 30 miles towards Middleton-in-Teesdale.

It was from this field that 'sea coal' was shipped to London from medieval times, that name deriving partly from the fact that it was transported by sea and partly because the first supplies were washed up on the Durham beaches. As the easily-won supplies at the western end of the field were exhausted, the collieries migrated

eastwards much earlier than they did in Yorkshire and Nottinghamshire with Wearmouth Colliery in Sunderland being sunk to a depth of 1,725ft in 1825-35, making it the deepest coal mine in the world, a record it held for many years. The magnitude of such an engineering feat at that time can be gauged by the fact that Britain's first proper public railway, the Stockton & Darlington, didn't open until 1825 and Stephensons' *Rocket* wasn't built until 1829.

In 1911, the Great Northern Coalfield produced a staggering 56million tons. It all came to an end in 2005 with the closure of Ellington Colliery following an underground flood.

North of Amble, there is only one tiny field - the Scremerston, near Berwick-upon-Tweed - until one reaches the central lowlands of Scotland, when they reappear with a vengeance. This area of Scotland, like Durham and South Wales, was peppered with collieries at one time, but there are two significant features that characterise Scottish coalfields.

Firstly, some of the deposits had their properties altered millions of years ago by the action of volcanic larva thrusting up through the seams, and secondly, not all the seams lie in the coal measures... just under half of them are found embedded in carboniferous limestone.

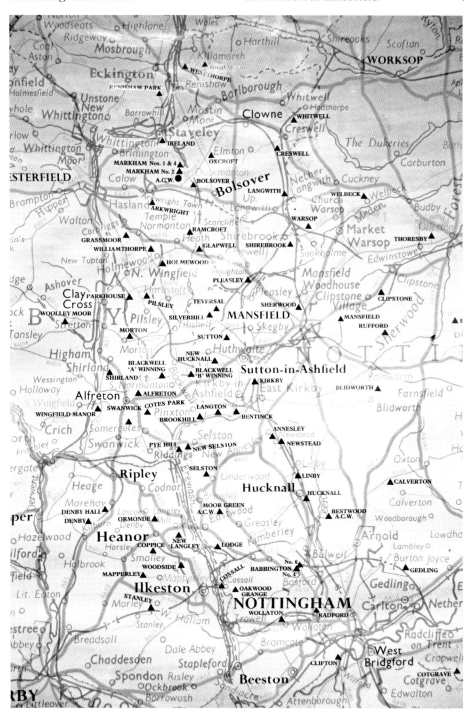

ABOVE: The extent of the East Midlands coalfield can be seen in this map from the early National Coal Board era. Almost 100 collieries are visible between the Nottingham district and the Notts/Derbys/Yorkshire border – and this excerpt doesn't even show Ollerton, Bevercotes and Bilsthorpe mines, which lay to the east of Thoresby.

ABOVE: The Northumberland part of the Great Northern Coalfield is today represented by the preserved Woodhorn Colliery, which also houses the county's Records Office. NICK PIGOTT

ABOVE: The most northerly coalfield in Britain was the small Brora field, which lay in the county of Sutherland, almost 40 miles north of Inverness as the crow flies. Unlike the great majority of British coal, which was laid down in the Carboniferous Period, Brora deposits belonged to the more recent Jurassic Period. The colliery closed in 1969 but the measures continued to be worked from nearby drifts until the mid-1970s.
RIGHT: The Kingdom of Fife possessed substantial coal deposits and boasted some 30 pits in NCB days, several of which were served by the Wemyss Private Railway, whose Barclay 0-6-0T No. 20 is storming out of Methil West yard in 1967. W J V ANDERSON/RAIL ARCHIVE STEPHENSON

Coal that came into contact with igneous molten larva was converted by the forces of nature into coke or anthracite, the latter being more valuable than ordinary bituminous coal.

There are four main regions of Scotland in which coal was mined – Ayrshire, Lanarkshire, Midlothian and Fife – but the disjointed nature of the occurrences has resulted in several separate coalfields, some sub-divided.

The **Lanarkshire** (or **Central**) field is the largest, extending from Glasgow and Lanark up towards Stirlingshire and at its peak producing 17million tons of coal, about 60% of Scotland's output. In addition, it produced fireclay and ironstone for the nation's industries and blast furnaces.

The next largest is the Fife coalfield, which ran for about 30 miles along the north bank of the Firth of Forth. For centuries, outcropping coal was collected on the seashores of the area and some of the colliery coalfaces extended under the sea.

The coal measures extended beneath the Firth of Forth to become the **Lothian** coalfield on the south bank, a

few miles east of Edinburgh, and it is in this field that the Scottish Museum of Mining can today be found in the former Lady Victoria Colliery at Newtongrange.

A small coalfield, just six miles by four and known as the **Clackmannan**, lies to the west of the Kingdom of Fife and the very last operational colliery in Scotland, Longannet, was situated about four miles south-east of Clackmannan. It closed in 2002.

Other minor coalfields in Scotland were the Canonbie, Sanquhar, Girvan, Douglas Valley, Machrihanish (on the Mull of Kintyre) and Brora, the last of which is interesting in that it is the most northerly coalfield in the whole of the British Isles. Situated in Sutherland, some 50 miles north of Inverness, its coal is of Jurassic origin formed only 160million years ago and consequently not of the highest quality. It was mainly used locally to supply a brickworks, distillery and woollen mill. Brora Colliery was nevertheless considered important enough to be modernised with pithead baths in the late 1930s and it survived as a private mine licensed

by the National Coal Board, not closing completely until the early 1970s.

This just leaves one established British coalfield to be dealt with – the one that surprises most people when they are told about it for the first time. It is the **Kent** coalfield, an anachronism in the 'Garden of England'.

It wasn't even discovered until the late-Victorian era and then only as the result of an assumption by mining engineers that the large coalfield of northern France and Belgium might continue under the English Channel. In 1890, boreholes were sunk near Dover's Shakespeare Cliff by a company involved in an ill-fated Channel Tunnel rail scheme and the hunch was indeed confirmed.

Nine mines were built to tap into the field's 14 seams, but the first of those, Dover Colliery (sometimes known as Shakespeare Colliery), was not a success and was closed after just a few years in 1915, as were the mines at Guilford and Cobham. Stonehall (also known as Lydden) and Wingham were abandoned without ever producing coal but the other four – Snowdown, Betteshanger, Tilmanstone and Chislet

– were far more successful and long-lived. The latter was a large mine modernised by the National Coal Board in the early 1960s and notable for featuring an underground overhead electric railway system.

All four NCB pits in Kent were built on a large scale with headgears and winding engines of massive construction to deal with the extreme shaft depths of more than 3,000ft, but only continuous pumping enabled them to cope with the salty water found in the strata.

Kentish coal mining came to an end with the closure of Betteshanger in August 1989 and it was thus the shortest-lived of all the significant British coalfields. ●

● In addition to those detailed above, there is a concealed coalfield beneath parts of Oxfordshire and Berkshire that has never been commercially exploited plus a little-known field near Bovey Tracey, in Devon, but the latter contains lignite, rather than fully formed coal, and is therefore the only deposit found in England that does not date back to the Carboniferous Period.

The Coal Mine on the Beach

Dover Colliery, Shakespeare Cliff.

ABOVE: The English coalfield most isolated from the rest was located in Kent and in NCB days possessed four major collieries – Chislet, Tilmanstone, Snowdown and Betteshanger. Few people are aware that there had at one time been other mines in the 'Garden of England', the biggest of which was Dover Colliery, known as 'the Coal Mine on the Beach'. Its remarkable position at the foot of Shakespeare Cliff can be appreciated in this early 20th century postcard photograph.

SETTING THE STAGE

COAL has been known to man since the dawn of civilisation and there is carbon-dated evidence of it being used for cremation pyres in what is now Wales about 3,000 years before the birth of Christ. Bronze-age axe heads have been found embedded in coal and excavations of Roman sites in Britain have found traces of coal ash, indicating that it was used in a modest way during the military occupation of 43 to 410AD.

The Romans are known to have smelted iron using local coal and ore at their fort in Caerleon, near modern-day Newport, and had discovered outcrops in the Somerset coalfield too, for there is evidence of coal being used in the city of Bath to fuel hot springs and feed a sacred flame in the Temple of Minerva.

More than 400 years after the Romans left Britain, the chronicles of Peterborough Abbey reveal that 12 loads of 'fossil coal' were purchased in the year 852, but the Domesday Book of 1086 makes no mention of the mineral, even though lead and iron mines are recorded, and it is not until the 13th century that documents show 'sea coal' being sent to London by sailing vessels from the north-east of England.

In those days, coal was not mined in the modern sense but retrieved; either by collecting it from shores and beaches where it naturally washed up with every tide or by burrowing into riverbanks and other shallow locations.

Burrowers (the forerunners of modern drift miners) would dig what is known as an 'adit' and literally follow a seam into a hillside for as far as they dared before flooding, foul air or the risk of a collapsed roof forced them to abandon the orifice and start another close by. When such naturally occurring supplies of coal became exhausted, vertical holes were dug into the surface of adjoining land and colliers hollowed out as much of the mineral as they could from the base before they too were threatened with the collapse of the soil above them.

Those holes were the first bellpits, so called because of their shape in profile (see illustrations). Initially, they were shallow enough for the coal to be carried out by ladder but as they grew deeper, hand-operated wooden windlasses were erected around the openings to winch baskets up and down on ropes. Although it might seem from a modern viewpoint that it would make sense to support the roof to prevent it collapsing, archaeological

evidence indicates that it was clearly considered quicker and easier to simply abandon a worked-out pit and dig a new one alongside.

Roof support did eventually come after it was noted in bellpits that had been 'holed through' underground to adjacent ones that the air was fresher and that a breeze was generated. This was the genesis of arguably the most

important aspect of the entire mining industry - the principle of upcast and downcast air flow - and it has dictated how mines and shafts are constructed ever since (see chapter 89).

The ventilated pits enabled the early colliers to venture further into the ground and although they learned to hold up roofs with props of timber, numerous collapses - and no doubt

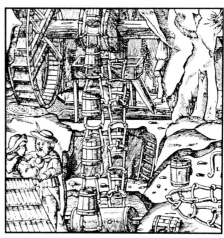

ABOVE: Before the invention of furnaces and fans, the only way a medieval miner could get rid of gas was to waft it out with a large cloth. As for water, rudimentary bucket chains driven by water wheels had to suffice until the arrival of pumps.

LEFT: The term 'bellpit' was derived from the shape of the excavation in cross-section, as shown in the illustration by John Berry on the facing page. In the early days, baskets of coal could either be raised by hand-winch or carried up ladders, as depicted in this model at Lady Victoria Colliery.

back to the shaft entrances grew longer, so women and children were hired to assist the menfolk by carrying or dragging the full baskets along the dark passageways and hooking them on to the windlass rope.

As more and more sections of coal were removed from between the supports, the subterranean scenes began to resemble honeycombs of rooms and pillars, hence the term 'room & pillar mining' (also known as pillar & stall, bord & pillar or stoop & room).

The disadvantage with the pillar & stall system, of course, was that it was dreadfully inefficient, for only about half the coal was mined, the rest being left untouched in the ground, yet ▶

injuries and deaths – made them realise that it was safer to leave blocks of coal in situ as support pillars. These allowed them to make incursions into the seam on all four sides as well as advance further into the terrain in relative safety. The size and shape of the pillars (also known as 'stoops') was a matter of skill and careful judgment and depended on the depth of the working and the nature and hardness of the roof.

The spaces between the pillars were known as stalls. Most were too small for two hewers to work in, lest they accidentally struck each other with their picks, but some hewers chose to work with a mate, who would fill the tub with the loose coal he had cut. As they advanced, the distances

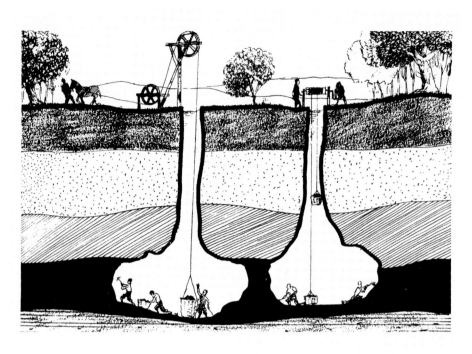

ABOVE: An illustration of an 18th century scene showing the transition between the windlass-operated type of bellpit and the horse-powered pulley wheels that were to form the basis of the large steam and electricity-driven headstocks of the future. Note the closeness of the two pits, only a small pillar of coal supporting the roof.

resulting in pungent smoke swirling around the narrow cramped streets. Attempts were made to ban use of the fuel in London, but with little effect.

It might appear from this that Britain was already a coal-fired society in the 13th to 16th centuries, but nothing could be further from the truth. Coal accounted for only a minuscule fraction of the fuel burnt in the country at that time. The vast majority was wood, much of which was also being used to produce charcoal to supply Britain's fledgling workshops.

The amount of charcoal needed to smelt just one ton of iron for weapons or cannon required a whole acre of woodland to be destroyed, which is why suitable types of timber were becoming scarce. Exacerbating the situation in the 1500s and 1600s was the sheer volume of wood required to build the great Navy ships of the time (a single large warship required the timber of 4,000 oak trees), and laws were therefore passed protecting woods and forests from unauthorised felling.

Therein lies one of the main reasons for the future success of coal, for the effect was to make wood and charcoal prohibitively expensive... so much so that in the 1590s, the price of firewood rocketed by 800%, causing the English Parliament to ban the use of charcoal for all but the most important uses and encourage the population to burn coal instead.

Up until that point it had still been relatively small fry - a mere 210,000 tons produced annually in the entire country... less than the output of a single medium-sized colliery 300 years later.

despite that it is still deployed in some parts of the world today.

Records of the 12th century that have been passed down to us show that wood, charcoal and peat were the fuels universally employed in the British Isles at that time. In the homes of the common people, a peat or wood fire would lie in a hole in the floor, exhausting through a hole in the roof and to prevent the wooden houses from burning down at night when the inhabitants were asleep, a law was introduced whereby a bell would be rung at dusk telling everyone to cover

their fire (*couvre feu*), from where the word curfew originates.

By 1257, many urban dwellers had switched to burning coal from the North Eastern and Scottish coastal areas (the so-called 'sea coal') and towns were beginning to suffer so much from the effects of smoky environments that Queen Eleanor felt forced to cut short a stay in the coalfield city of Nottingham, complaining of foul-smelling fumes. The problem was that most of the primitive little houses in the cities didn't have proper chimneys,

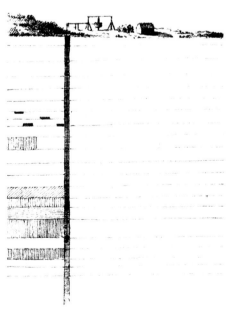

ABOVE: Before the advent of very deep mines in the mid-19th century, British coalfields were peppered with a plethora of shallow pits, as depicted in this typical hillside scene near Wednesbury, West Midlands, in April 1754. It was sketched by Reinhold Angerstein, a Swedish industrial spy who made a journey to Britain in the 1750s to gather information on the fledgling Industrial Revolution for his government.
ABOVE RIGHT: This other drawing of Angerstein's shows the sort of depths mines were reaching at that time – deep compared with bellpits but still extremely shallow in comparison with the huge collieries that were to proliferate in the next century.

ABOVE: This is how a typical rural coal mine would have appeared in the late 1700s/early 1800s. Winding of coal and men was done by a horse 'gin' in the centre of the picture and the coal would be taken away on the narrow gauge railway on the left and also by packhorse, two of which appear to be arriving in the foreground. ('Gin' was a short form of the word engine.)

The year 1604 saw Britain's first waggonway built to convey coal from Strelley pits to Wollaton, just west of Nottingham. Similar forerunners of railways quickly appeared in the North East, operated with horse-drawn chaldron waggons. Also becoming commonplace in the 17th century were horse-powered 'gins', comprising a geared cog & drum assembly to wind rope up and down a shaft.

In certain coalfield areas at about that time, the sides of many hills and valleys were peppered with small holes, above which stood gins or windlasses. Most were simply abandoned after the coal had been extracted and thus became serious hazards once their entrances had become partly obscured by long grass and bushes. There are many records of local people and livestock being injured or killed as a result of falling into old pits. Gradually, they were filled in but, with no record of where they all were, it took centuries for these man-made 'rabbit warrens' to be made safe. An idea of the size of the task can be gained from the fact that in 1947 the newly formed National Coal Board identified no fewer than 442 abandoned mine workings in the Sheffield area alone!

Another indication of how the industry was growing in the late 1600s could be gained from the number of 'collier' sailing ships employed in transporting coal to London from the Great Northern Coalfield of Durham and Northumberland. This shot up from 20 in 1550 to 900 in 1660, there being no quick or cheap means of moving large quantities of coal over land for such a distance until the great canal-building era arrived in the 18th century. In fact, it was revealed in 1675 that it was cheaper to move coal 300 miles by sea than it was to move it 20 miles by horse.

In the early 1600s, it was reported in the vernacular of the time that "sea-cole and pitt-cole is become the general fewell of this Britaine island, used in the houses of the nobilitie, clergy and gentrie in London and in all other cityes and shires of the Kingdome as well as for dressing of meate, washing and brewing".

Coal was indeed starting to become a significant player in the commercial fabric of the nation and the era of deeper mining was beginning to dawn, with some pits being dug down to 200ft. That is when methane gas (known colloquially as 'firedamp') and prevalent in most mining districts, began to be a problem because the only way to prevent it was for a 'fireman' dressed in thick, water-soaked clothing to go down into the pit at the start of each day and explode the pockets of gas with a candle on a long pole... or with a candle pulled along with a string while he hid in a hole. Such bravery cleared the danger, but only for a few hours at a time.

To ventilate the mines on a longer-lasting basis, fire baskets (later replaced by furnaces), were placed at the bottom of the upcast shafts so that the air currents caused by the flames would draw air through the mine workings, but there was always a risk that it would become charged with methane while travelling through the passageways and explode when it reached the furnace. This remained a problem until the furnaces were eventually replaced by fans.

By 1700, pits had reached depths of 360ft, almost all worked on the room ▶

> "MANY PEOPLE AND ANIMALS DIED FALLING INTO OLD PITS. IT TOOK CENTURIES TO FIND ALL THE HOLES AND MAKE THEM SAFE"

ABOVE: Railways arrived on the scene long before locomotives. In well-established mining areas such as the North East, large waggons such as this were used to convey coal from pit to port. Loaded waggons would usually be run down to the harbour by gravity (note the large handbrake lever for controlling the speed) with the horses being used for hauling empty vehicles back uphill.

& pillar basis with half the coal being left behind to support the roof - but the other big problem was the percolating of water into mines, for the depth a collier could reach was limited by the level of flood water.

So far, most pits and tunnels had been dug relatively close to the surface, staying above the natural water table. There were drift mines that had been dug into the sides of notoriously wet hills but the drifts

usually ascended slightly so that a) the water would drain away into the valleys of its own accord and b) it would ease the task of hauling the loaded coal from the face to the exit of the mine. In locations where it was not always possible for the main haulage road to ascend, a smaller adit would be driven to the outside of the hill or valley to act as a drain.

Vertical shaft pits, however, had to rely on a bucket-and-chain system, either using the same shaft as the coal (which hampered production) or an adjacent shaft, operated usually by a horse-powered drum and chain using suitable gearing. In many places, though, the sheer volume of water was becoming a major problem.

Although several experiments had been made with crude water pumps in the 1600s, it wasn't until 1712 that Thomas Newcomen produced the first efficient atmospheric engine to drain mines of water. The colliery at which the pioneering machine was installed is believed to have been at Coneygree, near Dudley Castle in the West Midlands. It worked not as a steam-driven engine but by using the pressure of the atmosphere to push a piston against a partial vacuum created in the cylinder by condensing the steam. Its efficiency was less than

ABOVE: Some of the thickest coal seams in Britain were found in Staffordshire, where the height of 12 to 14ft and more made It possible to undertake the room & pillar method of mining with the emphasis on 'room'! Miners crawling through 2ft high gaps in the thin seams of Lancashire and others could only dream of such spacious working conditions.

ABOVE: Most room & pillar mining was conducted before the advent of photography and, even afterwards, cameras were only allowed down mines under strict safety precautions. It was not until the introduction of opencast mining in the 1940s that unexpected surprises such as this began to come to light. This example was unearthed at Blindwells, in East Lothian, Scotland, and the large amount of coal left to support the roof shows just how inefficient some of those early mines were.

1%, but it could lift 10 gallons of water 153ft with each stroke of its beam – about 5,000 gallons an hour.

Over the next half-century, Newcomen-style machines of improving types, and more efficient James Watt-designed steam engines, spread across the nation's coalfields, reducing fuel costs and making mines more profitable for their owners.

The advent of the Newcomen pumping engine just over 300 years ago is thus generally considered to represent the birth of deep mining, although 'deep' is a relative term, for those crude early developments merely paved the way for the ultra deep-mining era of the 19th and 20th centuries that revolutionised the entire industry. Until then, it had been assumed by engineers that mining at depths greater than 350ft or so would always be unattainable due to water ingress.

We know that seams of about that depth were being accessed in the 1750s because they appear as illustrations in the diary of Reinhold Angerstein, a Swedish industrial spy who was sent by his government to travel extensively in England monitoring the extent of industrial progress in 1753-55.

In 1763, Walker Colliery, near Newcastle, took delivery of the largest engine in the world at the time – a Newcomen product with a 74-inch

cylinder that had been cast by the Coalbrookdale Company of Shropshire and could pump water from a then-unprecedented depth of 530ft. A major milestone was reached 17 years later at another Northumberland colliery, Willington, when a Watt-designed engine was used for coal-winding (as opposed to mine-draining).

Also appearing in mid-18th century chronicles was the first written mention of what was to become the main alternative to room & pillar mining – the longwall technique. This required rows of wooden props to hold the roof up while colliers standing alongside each other hewed coal from the face at a fairly uniform rate, in

> "A HUGE EXPANSE OF STRATA WAS LEFT EXPOSED ABOVE THE COALFACE AND MINERS HAD TO RELY ON THE STRENGTH OF WOODEN PROPS"

order to remove a layer of coal in a single operation. In doing so, they created what was literally a long wall.

This had the advantage that it recovered virtually 100% of the coal compared with 50-60% in room & pillar, but it was far more hazardous as it left a huge expanse of strata exposed above the coalface and relied on the strength and stability of the props and the skill of the colliers in positioning and inserting them correctly.

As the face advanced, thick stone walls (known as packs) were erected to help support the roof alongside the roadways, but the roof above the waste (known as the 'goaf' or 'gob') was allowed to collapse as long as there were no buildings above it.

Strenuous efforts had been made by engineers to tackle the problems of ventilation and flooding, but there was a third major obstacle that would need to be overcome before mining could really take off as a major industry – transport.

The Britain of that time had no proper roads, only unmetalled stagecoach routes and mud tracks, and the only way to shift coal long distances had been by coastal collier vessels. However, the second half of the 18th century marked a great canal-building era in the country, most with the carriage of coal as their prime objective. Well over 100 of these inland ▶

ABOVE: Not until Thomas Newcomen invented an atmospheric water-pumping engine in 1712 could mines be kept sufficiently dry to enable regular production. Rapid advances in the technology of stationary steam engines between then and the early 1800s produced more efficient and powerful engines and enabled the sinking of shafts below the water-bearing measures. This fine model is part of the Scottish Mining Museum collection.

ABOVE AND BELOW: The very first Newcomen engine of 1712 was installed at Dudley Castle, West Midlands. Today, just a mile away at the Black Country Living Museum, can be found this full-sized working replica. Note the beam on the left of the building and coal stocks on the right.

waterways were built in a relatively short space of time to enable the advantages of widely available coal to be felt in all parts of the country rather than just London and the coastal towns.

One canal, built by the Duke of Bridgewater to link his Worsley Colliery with the centre of Manchester, had reduced the cost of that pit's coal by no less than half, showing what enormous potential there was in reforming inland transport.

Railways as we know them would not arrive until the first half of the 19th century, although preliminary work had started on a horse-drawn railway at Middleton, Leeds, as early as the 1750s and within the internal layouts of numerous collieries themselves, waggonways with wooden rails were in fairly widespread use. The year 1767 saw the first use of cast iron for rails, at Coalbrookdale, and 16 years later came the first *bona fide* waggonway to be laid underground in a British colliery - at Sheffield Park Colliery, in Yorkshire.

This was a development of the primitive 'hund' system that had been used in central European mines since the late Middle Ages, a hund being a small, wheeled tub.

Until the beginning of the 19th century in Britain, coal had remained a largely local industry, operated by reasonably wealthy families and restricted by lack of a proper transport system to areas where naturally occurring outcrops and shallow seams could be accessed. It also tended to be contained within areas that were easily accessible to the sea or to canals and the social fabric of the country was changing with it, writer Arthur Young noting in 1791 that "all the activity in the kingdom is fast concentrating where there are coalpits."

While an unsuspecting population waited for the steam railway age to burst upon it and change the nature of the country for ever, coal shipments from the Great Northern Coalfield continued to grow and exceeded a million tons for the first time in the late 1700s. Swansea dock was also a big player, sending out a quarter of a million tons. The total amount of coal produced in Britain as a whole in the 1780s was just under 10.3million tons.

What is sometimes known as the 'First Industrial Revolution' had started circa 1760, fired largely by the availability of cheap and plentiful coal, and mines were becoming deeper and deeper. Percy Main Colliery had attained a depth of 960ft in 1799 - making it the deepest in Britain at that time.

The stage was set for the coming of the railways and the phenomenal growth in the coalmining industry that would see Great Britain become the 'workshop of the world'. ●

ABOVE: By 1800, mines had become so extensive underground that pockets of methane gas ('firedamp') lurking in the roof cavities were being encountered on a regular basis. The invention of the Davy and other safety lamps was still more than a decade away so until then, there was little else for it but to employ a 'fireman', whose job was to wrap himself in thick water-soaked garments, crawl forward with a naked flame on the end of a long stick and ignite the gas. Because of their monk-like hoods and short life expectancy, such men were known by their fellow mineworkers as 'the Penitents'.

ABOVE: As a taster for the chapter starting on the next page, this picture shows the vast rate of development that took place during the first half of the 19th century following the dawn of the railway age. The scene depicts the colliery and ironworks at Clay Cross, Derbyshire.

BRITAIN... WORKSH

ABOVE: The workshop of the Welsh Mining Museum at Big Pit in Blaenafon.

RIGHT: An indication of the colossal scale of Great Britain's coal-exporting industry in its heyday can be gained from this aerial view of Cardiff's Queen Alexandra Dock. The photograph is undated but was taken during the era of private colliery ownership, so before 1947. There are well over 1,000 coal wagons waiting to be unloaded and similar scenes would be enacted at other docksides in South Wales and at the many other ports serving the Northern and Scottish coalfields. Today, Britain imports coal despite having enough of its own to last hundreds of years!

IT is no exaggeration to say that the Industrial Revolution could not have occurred if it had not been for coal. If there had been no deposits in the British Isles, the great social phenomenon Britain gave to the rest of the world would have taken place in another country and probably much later.

The revolution might not even have started at all if Britain had not suffered serious deforestation in the 16th century, triggering laws forcing the population to start burning coal instead of wood and charcoal.

By the turn of the 19th century, all the building blocks were in place for

possibly the biggest social upheaval in the annals of human history.

Most historians put the genesis of the Industrial Revolution at 1760, some as early as 1700. Those, however, are the

ABOVE: An early 1820s sketch of Hetton Colliery and two of its George Stephenson-built locos.
RIGHT: The Stockton & Darlington Railway's first passengers rode on the coal as well as the wagons!

dates at which early mechanisation began to make its presence felt in the relatively modest workshops of the day, most of which were locally based and self-contained. It has to be remembered that the Britain of 1800 was still primarily an agricultural society. There was a relatively small population, no railways, no proper roads... hardly any means by which labour forces and heavy products could be moved around the country except on water or drawn by horses.

The Industrial Revolution scenes beloved of history and geography ▶

ABOVE: This fine classical painting by Victorian artist John Carmichael depicts Murton Colliery, County Durham, in 1843 and shows that tall headstock-mounted pulley wheels were by then in use (although an old-style horse gin can be seen in front of the largest building). The long-backed leather hat and waterproof over-garment worn by the man in the foreground indicates that he is a shaft-sinker, the hat being designed to prevent water running down inside the back of his collar.

teachers – of countless smokestacks belching out smoke, grimy goods trains and row upon row of terraced houses – still belonged to the future when the 19th century dawned on an unsuspecting England.

ABOVE: The opening of a new colliery was a grand occasion, often accompanied by a banquet for coal owners, local dignitaries and possibly even miners and their families. Such a gala is depicted in the grounds of Gyfeillion Colliery (later renamed Great Western Colliery) in August 1851. The Hetty shaft winding house of this mine has been preserved.

Richard Trevithick's idea of turning the concept of the coal mine water-pumping engine into one that could use wheels to propel itself along a track was still four years away and not even those with the most vivid of imaginations could have foreseen what a vast difference that invention would have made by the time babies born in 1800 reached their 100th birthdays.

Ironstone had been found in close proximity to coal in several locations, so much so that 90% of British iron was being smelted in South Wales by the time Trevithick's first steam locomotive took to the rails near Merthyr Tydfil in 1804. Other inventors soon began to improve on the design and by 1812, the Middleton Colliery in Leeds was operating the first commercial steam trains. Up in the North East, Wylam Colliery was experimenting with the rudimentary steam locomotives *Puffing Billy and Wylam Dilly*.

The big breakthrough on the world stage came in 1825 with the opening of the Stockton & Darlington Railway – generally accepted to be the world's first 'main line' route. It was an extremely successful venture, carrying 52,000 tons of coal by its third year and running more than 30 trains a day by the time the world's first inter-city railway opened between Manchester and Liverpool five years later.

Potential earnings from coal was one of the prime factors that fuelled the 'Railway Mania' in the 1840s, for the great coalfields of Britain were crying out for rapid connection with the major markets of London and the South East, and vice versa.

The railways are dealt with in more detail in a separate section starting on page 104.

By the 1850s, there were 2,397 collieries in Britain, but many of those were still small, primitive and grouped very close together, as evidenced by the fact that there were 516 mines in Staffordshire and Worcestershire – more than twice as many as in Durham and Northumberland, and yet the amount of coal they produced annually was well under half the 15million tons mined by the 225 collieries in the latter two counties.

Even Yorkshire possessed only 270 pits at that time but the spread of railways had seen the search for coal reach frantic proportions with 50 shafts being sunk close to Barnsley in quick succession and new seams being found at ever-greater depths. As with the railways, many fortunes were made during the coal equivalent of the 'gold rush' and towns in the region began to boom as Britons turned their hands to manufacturing virtually everything under the sun.

As early as the 1860s, 'experts' were predicting that, at such a rate of extraction, Britain's coal would

The Coal Owners

AS with any industry, there were good bosses and bad, but in the era of privately owned mines, a depressingly high proportion of coal owners drove their men hard for little pay and minimal rights.

Benevolent owners, on the other hand, cared for the well-being of their workforces and provided schools, chapels, free coal, electricity and water in addition to good quality housing, sports pitches, bowling greens and, in the case of Kiveton Park Colliery, near Sheffield, even a hospital.

Some of the pits were under the control of sizable combines such as Powell Duffryn, while others were owned by families – often the same family whose ancestors had first sunk the mine several generations earlier.

Miners employed by religiously aware Quaker families were paid regular wages and were provided with schools, shops, chapels and comfortable houses. The Tredegar Company was also a socially aware employer and built houses and hospitals at the turn of the 20th century.

soon run out, but more and more new seams were located and sleepy out-of-the-way villages were transformed almost overnight from agricultural to industrial ways of life.

In fact, so many new coalfaces were being opened up that the forests couldn't keep pace with the demand for pit props (shades of the deforestation crisis of the 16th century!) and timber had to be imported from Russia and Finland. The result was that by the end of the 19th century, the relatively little island of Britain possessed an estimated 3,000 coalmines.

Between 1862-80, some of the independent coal producers began to amalgamate and by 1864 the Powell Duffryn combine, with 59 pits and 30,000 employees, had become the world's largest coal producer, followed by Lewis Merthyr and the Ocean Coal Company.

The lives of the businessmen who ran such enterprises was a million miles from those of the men who toiled hundreds of feet beneath their feet. Although it had been made illegal for women and children to work underground since 1842 ▶

ABOVE: An 1814 view of Middleton colliery and railway, near Leeds. The painting, by contemporary artist George Walker, is entitled The Collier, but appears to depict him in his 'Sunday best'.

the hardships faced by men underground had changed little and despite the passing of numerous Parliamentary Acts designed to improve their lot, the 20th century dawned with thousands of them still having to risk death or injury from roof collapses, dust-clogged lungs and naked flames in gas-laden atmospheres.

In those days, many colliers worked in pairs and it was the job of the senior man and his helper not only to cut coal but also to advance the face and erect the pit props as they went. They also had to bore holes, break up the waste stone and pack it tightly in the previously mined void (the 'goaf') to support the roof as the face advanced further from the pit shaft.

Although the men were not always favourably inclined towards the work, they had great pride and respect for themselves for being able to perform such a tough task, year after year.

On top of all that, the early colliers had to buy their own tools (usually by deduction from wages) and had to lock them up at the end of every shift to prevent them being stolen by unscrupulous colleagues. At most collieries, the men were on piece-work and toiled under the control of a charter master or so-called 'butty', who paid them only for the stint they produced each day and often manipulated pay and working conditions to maximise their own profits.

Given such circumstances, it was unsurprising that unrest was rife. There had been numerous local strikes, lock-outs and other instances of dissent in the coalfields in the 19th and early 20th centuries but the first national strike of British miners occurred in 1912 and secured a minimum wage to ensure that colliers who worked in difficult seams weren't disadvantaged (see Strikes chapter, page 114).

> "AS EARLY AS THE 1860s, 'EXPERTS' WERE WARNING THAT THE RATE OF EXTRACTION WAS SO GREAT THAT BRITAIN WOULD SOON RUN OUT OF COAL"

Whether by coincidence or design, the very next year, 1913, turned out to be the all-time peak year for production in the UK and more than a million people were soon employed in the industry – about one in 10 of the entire working-age male population of the country at that time. When it is considered that workable coalfields only covered a relatively small proportion of the British Isles, the statistic takes on an even greater resonance.

Exports were booming too – in 1913/14, the pits of South Yorkshire alone sent seven million tons of coal through Hull docks, much of it to Russia, which at that time had not begun to seriously exploit its own vast coal reserves.

Britain had, until the turn of the 20th century, been the largest coal producer in the world and had only recently been overtaken by the USA, so the future of the pits, like the future of the British Empire, looked rosy. But a rude awakening lay ahead... just a few months later, the First World War broke out, destroying the UK's export trade almost overnight (it never fully recovered) and causing huge manpower losses.

Many miners, like other workers, enlisted for military or naval duty in huge numbers. For the young unmarried ones, it was an adventure, a chance to travel to foreign places they could never have afforded to visit otherwise. Miners made great soldiers, fearless and determined, as British military leader Sir Douglas Haig recognised when he said: "There are no more gallant or enduring men on the battlefields of France than the miners of Britain." *The Times* weighed in by thundering: "The pit has no mercy for the weedy or the timid."

The problem was that the rush to sign up for the forces left the collieries in disarray at precisely the time they *Continued on page 35*

DID YOU **KNOW?**

The maximum annual British output of 287 million tons in 1913 would, if placed into railway wagons, form a train so long that it would stretch almost four times around the world!

Women and Children

'NOT

ABOVE: An early Victorian view showing the perilous ascent women and young girls had to make in the shafts before the law change of 1842. Not only did they have to climb rickety ladders laden with heavy sacks but ran the risk of being injured or knocked off by coal falling from those above them.

'ORTH A LIGHT!'

ABOVE: Lads left home white at the beginning of their shifts and came back black! This picture is undated but is believed to date from late Victorian times, so this pair probably worked in the screens or a similarly dusty part of the surface mine.

ABOVE: Strain and misery etched on their faces, two shoe-less boys struggle to bring a heavily loaded tub out of a mine. Note how the rope of the first lad passes around the neck and between the legs. COURTESY COAL AUTHORITY

ONE of the most shameful episodes in the history of coal mining concerns the subterranean employment of women and very young children in the 18th and early 19th centuries.

Unfortunately, it has to be said that many of the private coal owners at the time were shameless when it came to the exploitation of their workers. Until prevented from doing so by law in 1842, they allowed women and children to work alongside men; they took a penny-pinching view to unsafe working practices such as naked flames and insufficient roof props… and they encouraged climates of fear in which colliers dared not speak out for fear they would lose their livelihood.

Children as young as four toiled in the pits and most were naked or near-naked due to the intense heat underground – as were the adults; a situation that naturally led to debauchery underground.

Many pregnant women suffered miscarriages by having to hew or haul coal 14 hours a day, six days a week for virtually the full nine months of their expectancy, but health & safety was of no consequence to the bosses, whose only consideration was profit. Life was cheap in those days and the workers were simply too impoverished to object.

This state of affairs had its origins in the primitive bellpits of earlier times when a self-employed collier hewing coal at his own risk and own expense would more often than not have his wife and kids carry the coal baskets up a ladder to the surface. While such work was being undertaken in the relatively shallow, light and airy environs of a bellpit, the problem wasn't too serious, but when deeper shafts and longer tunnels began to be developed, it became necessary for the helpers (who were rather ironically known as 'hurriers') to drag their heavy loads of coal while crawling on all fours along low, dark passageways.

For such work, a woman would usually be harnessed to a cart by a chain or rope that passed between her legs, even if she was pregnant. Some of the bigger children might also be engaged in such tasks, but mostly they were employed as 'trappers'. For this, kids as young as five would be dragged from their beds at 4

o'clock in the morning and made to sit for up to 12 hours or more in a cramped space about the size of a domestic fireplace, doing nothing but pulling on strings to open ventilation doors whenever anyone approached.

They were not even allowed to have a candle and had to sit in pitch blackness for the whole day, hence the phrase 'Not worth a light'.

In the early 1840s, Lord Shaftesbury went underground in South Wales and spoke to trapper boys. What he heard and saw shocked him so much that he resolved to return to London and press for reform. Politicians subsequently learnt that children were frequently taken down the mines by their parents, not only because they were keen for their offspring to strengthen their self-employed team, but because they were too young to be left on their own above ground.

In the 1830s, it is estimated that there were more than 5,000 children under the age of 10 working underground in such conditions and when, in 1838, 26 children (11 of them girls) were drowned in an underground flood in a disaster at Silkstone, in Yorkshire, a Parliamentary commission was set up in 1840 to look into working conditions in coal mines. The reports of the inspectors make for sober reading.

One sub-commissioner wrote: "It is a most painful thing to contemplate the dungeon-like life these little creatures are doomed to spend, a life for the most part in solitude, damp and darkness."

After seeing women struggling to drag iron-keeled boxes holding a quarter of a ton of coal, sub-commissioner Robert Franks commented: "It is almost incredible that human beings can submit to such employment, harnessed like horses, over soft slushy floors… more difficult than dragging the same weights through sewers in consequence of the inclination, which is frequently as steep as 1-in-3 to 1-in-6."

Another inspector reported: "The heat in the mine is so great that the men work totally naked in some cases, surrounded by females of all ages, from girls of six to women of 20, with many of the females also naked to the waist. So covered in coal dust and ▶

ABOVE: Children whose job it was to move the tubs were known as 'putters'. Whether due to artistic licence or not is unknown, but this drawing seems to depict youngsters little more than three or four years of age pushing a loaded tub underground while another not much older pulls open a heavy wooden ventilation door. Although the artist has in this case depicted a candle, the reality was far different as the poor air-door boys normally had to sit in the dark for their entire shift, hence the phrase 'Not worth a light'.

ABOVE: Male and female hewers working naked in a hot mine.

sweat were the boys and girls that their sex was only recognisable by their breasts. I had some difficulty on occasions pointing out which were girls and which were boys and that caused a great deal of laughter and joking."

In another report, it was stated: "The colliers are naked apart from a pair of clogs or hobnail boots and a thin pair of drawers, but sometimes the heat is so oppressive that even the drawers have to be discarded."

And one clearly shocked sub-commissioner wrote: "One of the most disgusting things I have ever seen was of young females, dressed like boys in trousers, crawling on all fours, with belts round their waists and chains passing between their legs, in pits near Holmfirth and New Mill. Two of the girls had worn large holes in their trousers and any sight more revolting can scarcely be imagined than those girls at work – no brothel can beat it."

The language in the pits was said to be bawdy in the extreme, with the women often being more foul-mouthed than the men. Noted one inspector: "It is impossible for a woman to be decorous or genteel in such conditions" while a Justice of the Peace from Yorkshire who visited one of his local pits as part of the inquiry said: "It is little wonder that passions are naturally excited."

After hearing that numerous illegitimate children were being conceived in the coal mines of Britain, Parliament passed the Mines & Collieries Act of 1842 prohibiting boys under the age of 10, and all women and children, from working underground.

Unfortunately, the new law was not backed up immediately by the appointment of a sufficiently large team of inspectors, which enabled some of the more unscrupulous mine owners to continue employing willing females for a few years longer. Sadly, there was

no shortage of girls prepared to turn a blind eye to the law in order to earn a few shillings at a time when money in other occupations was hard to come by.

Generally speaking, though, most colliery companies abided by the law, and the result was a massive increase in the number of pit ponies deployed underground (see separate chapter).

Boys over 10 continued to work, mainly in seams that were too thin for a grown man to crawl into, but attendance at school was made compulsory by Parliament in the 1860s.

Women were allowed to continue working on the surface, often as 'pit brow lasses' picking stones from the coal in the washery screens, and it wasn't until as recently as July 1, 1972 that the last two retired from Haig colliery, in Whitehaven. Somewhat ironically, equal rights legislation in recent years enabled women to return to subterranean work if they wished, although very few took up the option.

ABOVE AND RIGHT: After the law change of 1842, women could continue in colliery employment but only on the surface, where they became known as 'pit brow lasses' and were most usually to be found working in the coal washeries.

Continued from page 32
needed to be increasing production to keep the nation's steelworks supplied for the manufacture of tanks, cannon and other armaments. So, in 1916, the Government put the industry under state control to ensure continued supply of coal during the hostilities.

One unusual aspect connected with the war concerned a group of German workers who had been sinking the shafts of a new mine at Harworth, north of Retford. Their employer's assets were impounded by the Government and some historians report that the workers were interned for the duration of the hostilities, although some of them are believed to have scurried back to Germany at the last moment. Either way, the Harworth work was continued after the Armistice by new British owners.

Putting Britain's collieries into public hands during the war had given many miners a hope that they would be nationalised after the war, but in 1919 they were handed back to the private owners, contributing indirectly to another bitter strike in 1921. A triple alliance between miners, railwaymen and transport workers fell apart and the three-month dispute left the miners on poorer terms.

Just five years later came the General Strike, affecting industries in every walk of life, but that was called off after just nine days, leaving the miners to continue alone for six months until hunger forced them back.

The situation was exacerbated by the mass unemployment that resulted from the global recession of the late 1920s and the 'Hungry 30s' and by 1932, employment in mining had fallen by more than a third from its pre-strike peak of 1.2million. Colliers would be seen sitting by the side of the road eating bread and dripping and their kids would be playing in the street with no shoes on their feet because the families couldn't afford to clothe them properly.

The industry was in the doldrums relative to what it had been 20 years earlier and few pits were making a profit due to cut-throat competition between mining companies. The writing had started to appear on the wall a few years earlier for some of the older collieries in the west and central parts of the country. It was clear that their reserves were finite and so boreholes had to be sunk further east in an attempt to maintain production and close the inefficient mines in the west.

The effects of the 1930 Coal Mines Act resulted in 1923 railway grouping-style amalgamations for some colliery companies, such as Powell Duffryn Ltd (formed from 14 companies with 43 mines), Amalgamated Denaby Collieries Ltd (a merger of four colliery companies) and the Lambton, Hetton & Joicey Collieries Co, formed

ABOVE: Until the 1830s, the majority of steam locomotives built in Britain were for colliery or associated use. Such a machine was this 1822 vintage Hetton Colliery 0-4-0, which was still working when photographed for *The Railway Magazine* in 1905. In its early years, it had been a contemporary of the famous and now preserved 'Puffing Billy'.

ABOVE: Pitmen at a North Eastern colliery take a break from their duties to pose alongside a rake of chaldron waggons in the late 1800s.

ABOVE: A rare colour picture of tandem headstocks, which operated many mines before the Coal Act of 1912 made it illegal to build new collieries with timber-framed winding towers.

Hardships were all part of the job

'THE Devil made coal, made it black like himself and hid it in the deepest recesses of the earth so that he might drive men mad in the finding of it." That quotation from an unknown 19th century collier encapsulates much of the problem miners faced on a daily basis.

As if a job that involved crawling and working in wet seams as low as 2ft was not difficult enough, there were myriad additional impositions on the old-time colliers until the advent of the National Coal Board brought standardisation of working conditions across the country.

Hard though it may be to believe today, many colliery companies forced their miners to pay a weekly sum for the hire of lamps and that continued to be the case at some 'unenlightened' mines until as late as the 1930s. The policy was imposed even though the men couldn't see to do their jobs without a lamp, so they had no choice but to hire them and, at threepence or sixpence a week, they effectively paid for the original purchase price many times over. Even if a miner broke his pick or shovel while at work, the cost of the replacement was normally deducted from his wages.

Eyes and ears suffered terribly in the days before visors and ear defenders were issued. Sharp slivers of coal flew every time a pick slammed into a seam or a large lump, dust and grit swirled into eyes, nostrils and mouths, and if a lamp or candle went out in a part of the mine in which a man was alone, there would be no point at which his eyes would ever grow accustomed to the pitch darkness until he could reach an illuminated part of the mine. That could prove disorientating and frightening to anyone but a hardened collier.

Eardrums took a hammering once mechanisation began to be introduced to certain mines, for although the machines sped up the process, they made a deafening racket in the confined space below ground. They also made the operation more hazardous, not only because the noise disguised tell-tale creaking sounds in the roof but because the increased rate of extraction left dangerously large stretches of roof unpropped for longer. This was exacerbated by the vibration of the machines shaking everything loose. (This was in the days before huge powered, self-advancing roof supports had been invented.)

Many of the hardships encountered before nationalisation are not immediately apparent to a non-miner. Take clothes, for instance, in the days before pithead baths when miners had to change and wash at home: unless it was a very hot pit that caused men to strip to their underpants to work, the normal physical exertions would result in shirts and trousers being so soaked in sweat and dirt at the end of every shift that they'd almost stand up on their own when they took them off. But water was precious and sometimes only available from a well at the end of the street, so the clothes would not be washed, merely dried in front of the fire every night. Putting them on the next morning and walking or cycling to work in them must have been an uncomfortable experience to say the least.

On days when it rained, the coal dust that lay thick on the ground of the collieries would turn into a mass of cloying grey paste and on such occasions, sacks and cloths would have to be put down in the home to protect the furniture or floor coverings whenever work clothes were taken off.

Another hardship the men had to put up with occurred in the years when colliers were paid wages or bonuses on piecework according to the number of tubs they filled during the course of a shift. In a tightly run mine, the tubs returned from the shaft on a regular basis and there was no problem but in too many badly managed pits there were long delays and shortages of returns of trams, leaving colliers at the coalface angry, frustrated and even sometimes idle. Consequently, it was perhaps only human nature for fights to break out for the right to claim a tub and take it back to their stall.

Where a deputy (foreman) was on duty, this would not be a problem as he would decide who got the next 'tram' – although they had their personal favourites among the men and that often resulted in unfair treatment. Some deputies were more despised than the mine's owners and some were downright cruel and deceitful.

Bert Coombes, a miner from South Wales at around the time of the First World War, tells of one who ordered a team of repairers to clear a bad roof fall that was preventing loaded tubs from being sent out of the mine. The repairers told him the hole in the roof was still dangerous and that they would need to shore it up with timber supports before they could start to clear the obstruction. The official, however, threatened them with the sack if they didn't get the rocks removed straightaway.

Fearful for their jobs, they reluctantly agreed. The result: another roof fall and the crushing to death of an experienced repairer.

After the body had been removed, the foreman, thinking he was alone, was seen placing timber in among the rocks before the investigators arrived in order to make it look as though he had agreed to the repairers' original request. That would have been in a bid not only to save his own skin but to salve his guilty conscience… for if a death could be shown to be accidental, a widow would receive compensation, but if there was even a hint of negligence, the insurers would not pay a penny.

There was no pension scheme in those days either, so many older men – many with dust-clogged lungs – had to keep on working, desperate that the deputies or under-managers would not notice that they were coughing frequently and could no longer keep up the pace. The only money they could get to keep themselves alive in the pre-welfare state was 'parish relief' – a poor reward for a lifetime of hard and dangerous toil.

Housing shortages and, in later years, pit closures presented the additional hardship of travelling to other collieries in order to keep working. That would entail a trek of anything up to five miles on foot and in all weathers over the mountains that separated one valley from the next, or a train journey of up to 20 miles, often having to change trains in order to access a more distant valley. In the first 10 years of the 20th century, Wales had been a boom area with

by a merger of local mining companies in the North East. Unlike the railway groupings, the amalgamations were voluntary.

A drift to the east was also taking place a little further north, where Barnsley's traditional position as the centre of the South Yorkshire coal industry was coming under threat from the Doncaster and Rotherham areas, where deeper and more modern pits were being sunk in virgin territory.

On the other side of the Pennines, the situation was even more pronounced and mining in the Cheshire field ceased as early as 1935 due to thin and worked-out seams.

However, the new pits in the East Midlands and Yorkshire could be as deep as half a mile and thus extremely hot with low air pressure and many miners who had transferred from the

> "THE DEVIL HID COAL DEEP IN THE EARTH SO THAT HE MIGHT DRIVE MEN MAD FINDING IT"

shallower, cooler mines in South Wales, west Derbyshire and the North West couldn't handle the harsh conditions and left the industry.

For the collieries whose owning companies managed to withstand the worst ravages of the '30s, life could still be pretty good if the men could stomach the strict rules of the company-owned communities many of them had to live in. There were modernised collieries employing more than 1,000, working 24 hours a day, with compressed-air engines and roadways almost as high and safe as a main line railway tunnel, steel-arched and brick-lined.

ABOVE: Any young 21st century reader doubting that conditions and risks in some mines were as bad as described need only look at this picture to be convinced. It was taken in a British colliery in the National Coal Board era and shows a miner crawling through coal-blackened water as he negotiates his way through a 2ft seam. Only three dubious-looking wooden pit props protect him from the millions of tons of rock above him. Enduring similar situations in earlier times, his Victorian predecessors would not even have had the comparative 'luxuries' of helmet, cap-lamp, overalls, gloves and knee protectors.

tens of thousands of people migrating there from the worked-out or poorer-paying mining areas of Somerset, Gloucestershire and Cornwall, the latter being mainly former tin miners, as there was no coal in the Duchy.

In Victorian and Edwardian times, many miners had taken their sons underground with them and taught them everything they knew, but by the 1930s, most were adamant that their boys should go into anything other than mining, with its dangers and low wages. That attitude changed somewhat from the 1950s onwards when conditions and pay scales improved under the NCB and a lot of young men began to be attracted into the profession once more.

Like a **mental** picture of **hell**

MINES and miners have fascinated people from many different backgrounds, particularly writers and poets. In the 1930s, author George Orwell, an Eton-educated Southerner, visited collieries in Wigan, Sheffield and Barnsley to gain material for his book *The Road to Wigan Pier*, and gives a graphic description of the life he found there.

"When the machines are roaring and the air is black with coal dust... the place is like Hell, or at any rate like my own mental picture of Hell," he wrote. "Most of the things one imagines in Hell are there – heat, noise, confusion, darkness, foul air and, above all, unbearably cramped space."

Orwell, a tall man, told how he started off walking in a slightly stooped way but then had to crouch, squat and finally crawl as the height of the roadway gradually reduced from six feet to three. By the time he reached the face, he was in agony in his knees, thighs, back and head, which he had grazed numerous times on the jagged stone roof.

"Before I'd been down a mine, I had vaguely imagined the miner stepping out of the cage and getting to work on a ledge of coal a few yards away,' he wrote. "I had not realised that he may have to creep through passages as long as from London Bridge to Oxford Circus."

Despite the hardships, he noted how proud the Northerners were of their industrial heartland and that the miners of Lancashire and Yorkshire treated him with a kindness and a courtesy that were even embarrassing. "If there is one type of man to whom I feel myself inferior, it is a coal miner," he wrote.

▶

They were the exception rather than the rule, though; in South Wales, the total of miners slumped to 136,000 and production in that part of the UK was down to 35m tons.

It took the Second World War to change everything completely. Jobless miners flocked to enlist in the armed forces and, ironically, the industry moved from having tens of thousands of unwanted men to a serious labour shortage. As there was a renewed demand for coal to help the country re-arm in the face of the Nazi threat,

the Government made mining a reserved occupation to prevent any more men from joining up and then, in 1942, took control of the entire industry just as it had in the First World War.

A new Coal Act decreed that all coal reserves in Britain belonged to the nation for the duration of the hostilities, although the mining industry itself remained in private hands. The only exceptions were coal deposits belonging to Forest Free Miners in Gloucestershire and very thin seams at locations where other minerals were more

plentiful and more important than coal.

Even those moves didn't provide enough miners to meet demand, which led to the introduction of the Bevin Boy system (see panel).

Many pits had closed in the 1930s but some uneconomic ones were effectively subsidised by the more productive ones and were kept open after 1939 to contribute to the war effort, often being managed by more successful nearby companies.

Because there had been a feeling in the industry for many years that

A way of **Life**

MOST boys born in mining villages 50 to 150 years ago automatically went down the pit as soon as they were old enough. There was virtually nothing else for them to do.

Even in the early years of the 21st century, there were miners who had gone into the industry straight from school and never worked at anything else. Skills and camaraderie were handed down from generation to generation, generating fierce loyalty to the profession.

ABOVE: Something many colliers had in common with railwaymen was the requirement to work night shifts, but on a cold dark winter's night or after an evening 'on the ale', oversleeping was a problem. The coal companies therefore employed retired men as 'knockers-up', their job being to tap (or hammer!) on the doors and windows of miners' houses until they got a reply.

Despite the unregulated and rather haphazard nature of life in the 18th and 19th century collieries, there was nevertheless a sort of pecking order and succession policy; most young boys would start as trappers (before 1842) and then graduate from the age of about 12-14 to become a pony driver, leading a pony or horse as it pulled a rake of tubs through the underground passages.

After a couple of years doing that, he would become a 'putter' or 'hurrier', manhandling the tubs, both empty and loaded and ensuring that the hewers never had to wait for a tub to be delivered to their part of the face. While a putter, he would be given the opportunity to cut coal whenever possible and, at the age of about 21, he would finally attain the coveted position of hewer.

Night shifts meant that miners had to sleep at odd hours and in the days before alarm clocks and telephones, a 'knocker-up' would be employed by the colliery to go round the houses in the village and tap on the windows, often in the middle of the night. Knockers-up were usually old-timers or young lads and the railway companies also employed such people to ensure workers didn't accidentally oversleep.

In what little spare time they did have, miners played hard and, in common with their 19th century contemporaries, the railway-building navvies, had a fearsome reputation for heavy drinking and rebel-rousing... yet many were also God-fearing and would attend church with their families on Sundays. Unlike the navvies, who were forced by the nature of their work to be nomadic, colliers became rooted in close-knit communities that were to last for generations until mass car ownership from the 1960s allowed them to work miles away and meet potential partners from other areas.

One major nuisance for mineworkers (and something most members of the public were probably unaware of) was the problem of rats and mice underground.

The vermin mainly thrived on the sacks of grain and other foodstuff intended for the horses and ponies, along with scraps accidentally dropped by the miners, who had to ensure that their own packed lunches were kept out of the way, either by keeping them in tightly sealed metal tins or by suspending them in mid-air with lengths of string. The tight seals also kept out the all-pervading coal dust.

Some of the older mines were infested and it is ironically said with black humour that the only good thing about the year-long 1984/85 strike was that it rid the mines of mice!

A miner's packed lunch was known pretty universally throughout the country as 'snap' and usually comprised something simple such as jam sandwiches. No miner ate much underground in the old mines; the crouching position in which many of them had to work caused heartburn if the stomach was full. Even at home, some miners in the days before full mechanisation would occasionally feel the need to crouch or sit on a low seat in order to eat comfortably.

One thing they did take plenty of when going underground was water, usually carried in a sturdy flask known as a 'Dudley'. Some men preferred cold tea.

Bevin Boys: **Fighting Hitler at the Coalface**

AT the height of the Second World War, the British Government realised that so many men were enlisting to fight in the armed forces that there would soon be a shortage of coal for the war effort if the mines weren't adequately manned.

The Minister of Labour in the Coalition Government, Ernest Bevin, therefore decided that every 10th conscript aged 18 would be sent to the collieries, whether he liked it or not.

The 'Bevin Boy' system was introduced in December 1943 and between then and the end of the war in 1945, 21,800 youths were recruited and trained in the scheme, 7,000 of whom actually worked underground at the coalface.

The selection process was conducted fairly on a ballot basis and Mr Bevin went on record as saying: "None of you would funk a fight with the enemy and I do not believe that it would be said of any of you boys that you failed to respond to the call for coal upon which victory so much depends."

However, considering they'd had no choice in the matter and had been prepared to fight on the battlefields, they were treated very shabbily after the war and not allowed to march in the annual Remembrance Day parades at the Cenotaph in London – a situation that was not rectified until as late as 1995. Many of them also had to put up with abuse from ill-informed members of the public as a result of a mistaken but widespread impression that they were somehow 'shirkers' or conscientious objectors.

Among famous Bevin Boys were England footballer Nat Lofthouse and comedians Eric Morecambe and Brian Rix.

nationalisation was inevitable, the coal-owning companies had been reluctant to invest in new equipment with the result that the British mining industry had become uncompetitive compared with its German and American counterparts, especially where underground haulage was concerned.

By the end of the war, most people in Britain, regardless of political persuasion, accepted that the coal industry was worn-out, demoralised and in need of expensive modernisation. The Labour Party included nationalisation in its manifesto for the 1945 general election and won by a landslide.

The stage was set for the National Coal Board... ●

DID YOU **KNOW?**

Famous football managers Sir Matt Busby (Manchester United), Bill Shankly (Liverpool) and Jock Stein (Glasgow Celtic) all started work in the pits.

BELOW: In the absence of aerial colour photos of old-fashioned mines, the Scottish Mining Museum displays this model of Bannockburn Colliery, a typical medium-sized pit opened in the 1890s and closed eight years after the end of the Second World War. The winding house is on the left, the winding towers and heapstead roof in the middle, and the washery and screens on the right.

Pit Ponies Underground

CUDDLINESS and affection are not words that spring readily to mind when one thinks of collieries, but whenever mining museums stage family gala days, the most popular events with mums and kids are the pit pony rides.

Horses have been associated with mining since the earliest days, powering the revolving 'gin' wheels above the shafts in the years before headstocks, and hauling chaldron waggons back and forth between collieries and wharfs.

After the 1842 Commission banning women and young children from working underground, mine proprietors significantly increased the use of horses and ponies and found they were not only stronger but cheaper to run because, after the initial purchase, they required no pay other than food and stabling. This led regrettably to some mine owners taking the view that a human life was less valuable to them than a pony's.

Some mine companies with low roof clearances had to go to the extra expense of ripping rock from the top to give the animals room to walk, but that outlay often paid off, for higher roof clearances meant use of larger tubs and therefore greater productivity.

Even so, there were places in the roadways where the roof had converged, leaving jagged stones sticking downwards – yet the poor horses were still forced to pass through, having the skin on their back torn as a result. Most of the miners hated this torture the creatures had to endure but were too afraid to make a fuss. It was a case of putting the welfare of their wife and children before that of the pony.

A collier's productivity depended on his load being taken to the shaft as quickly as possible – yet in the bad old days no allowance was made as to whether the horse in his part of the mine was a fresh one or one that had just returned from another shift and was close to collapse from heat and exhaustion.

The underground stable blocks necessary to house so many beasts of burden were extremely extensive and it is still possible to get an idea of what they were like by visiting the preserved colliery at Blaenafon, in South Wales, which has 45 stables housed in two separate blocks. Built in 1890, they are surprisingly like open-air farmyard versions to look at, with brick whitewashed walls and the name of each horse or pony painted on a little nameboard on each stable door.

Although commonly referred to as pit ponies, only 10% of those used in Wales were technically ponies. Some of the largest horses were up to 15 hands (5ft) high.

At first, the animals could spend their entire lives underground, but in 1940, the Government passed a law requiring all horses to be brought to the surface once a year, usually at July/August time. Miners and pony-drivers were generally very proud of their charges and looked after them well given the difficult circumstances. If a pony began to go blind, it would be retired to grass at the more enlightened collieries, although others would put the animal down.

In 1913 there were 73,000 ponies engaged in underground work, by nationalisation in 1947, there were still 23,000 and as recently as 1984 there were more than 50 in use at Ellington Colliery, Co Durham, a few of which lasted until the 1990s. If all mines, rather than just NCB ones, are taken into account, the last colliery horses in Britain were probably Robbie and Gremlin, which were retired from a small private mine at Pant-y-Gasseg, near Pontypool, in 1999.

ABOVE: The bond between man and beast is readily apparent in this delightful study of Leicestershire mineworker Michael Gould and his pit pony, Neal. At one time, more than 70,000 horses and ponies were engaged on underground work in British collieries.

ABOVE: Passing in an unusually wide roadway are two horses and their minders, the white steed hauling three long pit props towards the coalface. As in most collieries, there was insufficient headroom for the horses to be ridden and in fact, most mine managements forbade such practice anyway.

THE NCB AND BRITISH COAL

ABOVE: A fresh start: The sign that went up at every colliery on New Year's Day 1947.

FOR the majority of miners, the National Coal Board was the promised land. After so many years of struggle against private owners, they would at last be working for themselves, stewarded by a Labour Government that 'spoke their language' and understood the reasons for their past struggles.

The company's motto *E Tenebris Lux* - Out of Darkness Cometh Light - articulated their hopes while the signs that went up at every mine on January 1, 1947 - 'This Colliery is now managed by the National Coal Board on behalf of the People' - set the tone for the monumental industrial and social changes that followed the horrors of the Second World War.

New Year's Day 1947, known throughout the industry as Vesting Day, was perhaps the most significant moment in the entire history of British coal mining. Overnight, the NCB became the largest non-communist industrial undertaking in the world, with 850,000 employees and just under a thousand collieries, some of which were enormous undertakings in their own right, utterly dominating their local communities. In Wales, the coal board was the largest single employer in the principality.

The whole exercise cost the nation's taxpayers the then immense sum of £394,365,176, including mineral rights, royalties, assets, stock and plant, but people on both sides of the political spectrum accepted that state ▶

ABOVE: Typical of the pits inherited by the National Coal Board was Penallta Colliery, in Wales's Rhymney Valley, pictured here in the early 1940s. The large message stating 'Search Yourselves' was a reminder to miners not to attempt to take cigarettes, matches or any other contraband below ground where it could cause an explosion. The winding towers and power house of Penallta Colliery still stand in 2016 but are derelict.

investment was the only realistic response to worn-out infrastructure, poor management, bad industrial relations, demoralised workers and shortage of capital.

In addition to the 958 collieries, there were 323 small licensed mines, 1,803 farms, 275 shops, 141,000 houses, a cinema, a holiday camp, hotels, swimming baths, brickworks, coking works, railways, ships and even a slaughterhouse.

The NCB didn't actually own the licensed mines, which were allowed to remain in private hands if they employed 29 or fewer underground workers each. Most were tiny drift mines and a fair proportion produced fireclay rather than coal. Between them, they represented a mere 1% of national annual output.

Where the coking plants and brickworks were concerned, the owners could negotiate to remain outside NCB ownership if they wished, and several took that option.

The NCB's first headquarters was Lansdowne House, Berkeley Square,

London, under chairman Lord Hyndley. The company was divided up into regions (known as divisions) and those eight divisions were sub-divided into

areas. Although the South Western Division, which contained South Wales, had the most collieries (230), the largest division was the Northern, which had

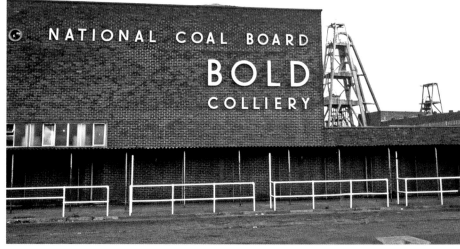

ABOVE: A suitably bold display at the entrance to Lancashire's Bold Colliery. In 1980 the yard of this mine was chosen as the venue for a gathering of main line and industrial railway motive power to mark the 150th anniversary of the Liverpool & Manchester Railway. COLOUR-RAIL

222 mines, 10 areas and contained the counties of Durham, Northumberland and Cumberland.

At local level, little changed straightaway because many of the NCB managers were simply the old private company officials wearing a different badge, but the board began to build up a technical management team and gradually started to get to grips with the neglect and lack of investment that had characterised the years of depression and war in the 1930s and '40s.

The UK needed coal to help fuel the national rebuilding programme after the war, so one of the first acts of the new board was to open a series of drift mines as a short-term measure while it prepared a massive programme of deep mine redevelopment as part of a root-and-branch reconstruction of the whole industry.

Modernisation, mechanisation and safety were the key components in the NCB's armoury and no expense was spared by the Government-backed board in instigating the necessary improvements.

Among the priorities in this brave new world were fully mechanised coalfaces, speedier transport of coal and men, skip-winding of coal from pit bottom to surface, new coal preparation plants, new coke ovens and greatly improved facilities for the men in the way of showers, changing rooms, canteens and, above all, personal safety.

From the miners' point of view, nationalisation had another benefit; it gave them, through their union, a greater say in their own industry.

Production soared as a result: In 1947, the average daily output per man shift had been 17.4 hundredweight; within the next 14 years it would double to 34.7cwt with men at some pits producing more than 50cwt.

Miners also had more freedom to move about, although in practice many stayed in the communities in which they'd spent their lives. There were enough changes going on as it was with all the boundary changes and frequent administrative upheavals. The NCB's 'county' districts, for example, bore little relation to real shires, with internal border changes resulting in the Nottinghamshire pits around Worksop coming under the Yorkshire district.

The modernisation and production gains came at a social as well as a fiscal cost, for they required a major rationalisation of infrastructure with many small, antiquated, run-down pits having to be closed, tearing apart communities as mining villages lost their prime raison d'etre. These closures were largely tolerated by the mining unions in the 1950s because they could see that they were an inevitable part of inward investment in their industry and there were also plenty of new jobs for displaced miners to move to if they wished.

ABOVE: Among the shadows cast by Ashington Colliery's washery screens on June 22, 1960 is British Railways Class J27 0-6-0 No. 65875. COLOUR-RAIL

ABOVE: Steam in Scotland: Unlike their main line cousins, which had to conform to a handful of standard liveries, NCB locos carried a plethora of shades and styles, although some did appear in the company's black & yellow corporate colour scheme. Such a loco was this Barclay 0-6-0T at Glenboig reception sidings, east of Glasgow in August 1978. The sidings served the nearby Bedlay Colliery, which closed three years later. GEOFF SILCOCK

Wages for those who remained in work were rising in the 1950s and by the end of that decade, face workers could earn £20 a week, putting them at the top of the blue collar wages league - a marked contrast to the 1930s. Many employees benefited from relatively high disposable income and it even became possible for them to afford cars, making it easier to take jobs in neighbouring towns and counties if they wished.

The NCB also improved the industry's poor safety record by expanding research into such matters as illness (particular pneumoconiosis) and dust control. Head protection was also greatly improved with soft caps being replaced by helmets made of compressed fibre board and later of tough plastic.

The socialist Government that had ushered in nationalisation of the mines and the railways after the war was replaced by a Conservative administration in 1951, but the nation's new rulers decided to let the NCB continue with its investment programme with the result that the Fifties was generally a good decade for 'King Coal'. At the beginning of the ▶

> "THE 1950s WAS GENERALLY A GOOD DECADE FOR THE INDUSTRY DESPITE THE CLOSURE OF MANY OLD AND INEFFICIENT PITS"

ABOVE: The chairman of the NCB from 1971 to 1982 was Sir Derek Ezra, seen here in the company of good-humoured miners during one of his many underground fact-finding visits.

next decade, however, both the coal and rail industries found themselves being run by hardline chairmen, the railways by Lord Beeching and the coal board by Lord Robens.

Beeching's tenure saw thousands of miles of branch lines closed and thousands of steam locomotives sent to the scrapheap; Robens presided over the closure of 406 mines and more than a quarter of a million jobs between 1961 and 1971, but for those remaining in work, he achieved 40% extra output, improved wages and reduced the number of fatal and serious accidents by 60%.

During Robens' 10 years in the chair, the industry had seen the greatest contraction in its history, falling from some 700 collieries in 1960 to just 299 in 1970. His 'axe' may not have been as infamous as its Beeching equivalent but it was just as devastating – or effective (depending on which political and economic standpoint it is viewed from). His tenure coincided with a rise of the militant Left in the National Union of Mineworkers, prompting Robens to make the thought-provoking comment: "One of the ridiculous aspects of the extreme left-wing in trade unions has always been their enthusiasm for strikes, whereas in the Soviet Union

and other Iron Curtain countries, strikes are illegal."

In 1969, the NCB was rocked by an unofficial dispute in which the men at almost half its 307 pits walked out, losing $2^1/_2$ million tons of coal production.

Some of Robens' decisions have been seen as bizarre in some respects. For instance, Kirkby Colliery was closed in 1969, only three years after proudly hoisting the union flag for breaking the million tons a year barrier, but there were reasons behind such decisions;

"SOME CLOSURES WERE CRAZY: AT ONE PIT, DEMOLITION OF NEW BUILDINGS WAS ORDERED BEFORE THE PAINT ON THEM HAD EVEN DRIED!"

Robens knew that over-capacity was a serious problem in the late 1960s and that some collieries had to go. His executives urged closure of old, inefficient pits in Wales, Scotland and west of the Pennines, but the chairman was aware that the NUM was a loose federation of nominally separate area unions. So, in order to secure acceptance of the cuts, he agreed that each area should lose one pit even though the Midlands and East Yorkshire had no really bad ones at the time.

This resulted in seemingly 'crazy' situations such as that at Kirkby – where contractors were still building a multi-million-pound coal preparation plant while NCB accountants were actively seeking tenders for its demolition! – and at New Lount Colliery in Leicestershire, where a brand new pneumatic stowing plant was still being painted on the day the mine closed... the new paint later clogging up the nozzles of the demolition crew's burners as they cut the plant up!

Most pits closed during that period were, however, inefficient and the policy improved overall productivity, although thousands of miners were thrown on to the jobs scrapheap in communities that could offer little else in the way of alternative employment.

By the late 1960s, the slimmed-down industry was still absolutely massive compared with what it was to become by the end of the century. It employed approximately half a million miners at 483 facilities and produced 177m tons of coal a year – but 1968 saw the end of steam traction on British Rail and, with millions of households switching to oil- and gas-fired central heating, coal was under threat. Even the NCB had replaced most of its (cheap to run!) steam winding house engines with electric equivalents.

Luckily, British Rail and the NCB worked together in the 1960s and '70s to implement a massive project to streamline the movement of coal from pits to power stations. Known as the 'Merry-go-Round' system (MGR), it saw construction of rapid-loading facilities at several modernised pits and installation of continuous-unloading hopper systems at the nation's major coal-fired power stations – especially those in the East Midlands and Yorkshire.

BR locomotives were fitted with radio control and slow-speed apparatus to allow them to haul 32-tonne hopper wagons through the power stations' automatic unloading bunkers at the required pace without the need for uncoupling and huge track loops were laid down so that the trains could continue around the circuit and head straight back to the colliery without the need for shunting.

MGR work gave the coal industry a new lease of life that was to last well into the 21st century, but it didn't stop the overall decline in the size of the NCB. By the mid-'70s, the number of deep mines was down to 240 – just a quarter of its 1947 total – with a workforce of less than 300,000. Productivity had increased 70% during Robens' decade but annual output had fallen to 114m tonnes

ABOVE: Hundreds of railway stations in Britain, both urban and rural, possessed a coal yard for domestic supplies. In this scene from 1968 – the year British Rail drove a nail into the coffin of its fellow nationalised industry by finally ridding itself of its steam locos – the coal yard at Woodley station, near Manchester, was doing a brisk trade as 8F class 2-8-0 No. 48115 passed with a Heaton Mersey-Godley Junction empty coal working. DAVID ROSTANCE/RAIL PHOTOPRINTS

and North Sea oil and cheap imports from the Middle East oilfields were beginning to take effect.

Robens was succeeded in 1971 by Sir Derek Ezra, who was to remain in charge for the next 11 years, steering a shrewd political course that maintained a reasonable balance between Government and unions.

As was the case with many of Britain's major industries in the 1970s, the decade saw union leaders taking a much greater role in the way the coalmines were run and the National Union of Mineworkers (NUM) had become one of the most powerful

unions in the land. Compared with the private-owner days prior to nationalisation, the boot was on the other foot for colliery managers.

The year 1972 had been hit by the first official national miners' strike since 1926, after which the Conservative Government of Edward Heath was obliged to accept wage demands that made the miners the highest-paid nationalised workers in the country. When a further pay demand was made just two years later, Heath put the country on a three-day week in a bid to conserve coal supplies and reacted to the start of another miners' strike by calling a snap general election, which, to the surprise of many, resulted in a change of Prime Minister (see page 114).

The miners' 1974 victory had given the country a Labour Government again, but it had unwittingly laid the foundations for their industry's ultimate demise, for those on the right-wing of British politics were determined that the NUM would never again be able to wield so much political power that it could effectively bring down an elected Government.

The 1970s strikes had also made businesses and householders realise just how dependent the country had become on coal to keep lights on, homes heated and the wheels of industry turning. Many individuals and companies began planning to switch to gas and oil, but just as they began doing this, the coal industry received an unexpected boost caused by a quadrupling of oil prices as a result of an Arab-Israeli war.

ABOVE: The concept of 'Merry-go-Round' trains was introduced by British Rail and the National Coal Board in the 1960s and revolutionised the power station coal supply business. In this October 1985 scene, a massive load of some 50 loaded MGR wagons is being hauled by BR Type 5 diesel locomotive No. 56089. JOHN CHALCRAFT

▶

No longer could the UK rely on seemingly endless supplies of cheap imported oil while deliberately running down its mining industry. North Sea oil supplies were still in their infancy, so the decline in indigenous coal production, which had been continuous since the mid-1950s, had not only to be halted but reversed.

That resulted in a decision in 1974 to re-invest in home-produced coal and one of the prime beneficiaries of that policy was the proposed Selby coalfield project in North Yorkshire – an exciting development of five new mines (primarily shafts only) that were to be linked underground by 124 miles of roadways connected by drifts to a huge central distribution facility

at Gascoigne Wood, a few miles east of the traditional West Yorkshire pits. The project was inaugurated by the Duchess of Kent in 1976 in a ceremony described as 'restoring King Coal to his throne'.

While the Selby complex was being constructed (it didn't fully open until the mid-1980s), a long-term contractual relationship was established between the NCB and the Central Electricity Generating Board for power station coal and the collieries of the UK began to enjoy a renaissance that was to last the best part of a decade.

Once the Middle East crisis had abated, the steady decline in the industry's fortunes resumed and reached a low point when a bitter confrontation over subsidy

withdrawals and pit closures resulted in the even longer and more aggressive 1984/85 miners' strike (see separate section on page 114).

Once the miners had been forced back to work, the retribution began with a vengeance. The initial pit closure programme was not only implemented but accelerated and by the mid-1980s there wasn't a single mine left in Wales's Rhondda valley. By the end of the decade, there were a mere two left in the whole of Scotland.

Britain had been an exporter of coal to power stations in France, Denmark, Portugal, Sweden and West Germany until the 1980s, but what remained of the overseas market was largely lost as a result of the strike and the situation

Why did some mines have the word **'Main'** in the name?

CAST your eye down any list of collieries and it will immediately become obvious that a large proportion of them incorporated the word 'Main' in their title.

Among the better-known ones were Yorkshire Main, Barnsley Main and Markham Main and it would be natural to assume that the word indicated a large colliery or one that tapped into the main (i.e. thickest or highest quality) seam in the area. However, mines without the word Main in their title often worked the same seams and as there were also numerous small and fairly insignificant collieries bearing this grand title, the reason was clearly not so straightforward.

The terminology does in fact date back to the early years of mining when private companies were struggling to establish themselves. The main pit would be the one that was considered by each firm to be the most important within its organisation. It might not have been the biggest mine the company owned, but it would be the one that either produced the largest output, the most profit or the best-quality coal – the latter being a reason for the firm to market its wares to the public as coming from the 'main' mine.

Even in those days, marketing was an important tool in the battle to establish a foothold in what was already becoming a highly competitive field and each rival company would have aspirations to be the leading coal producer in the area (whether it was or it wasn't!)

This led to a fair number of coal owners stressing the point by incorporating the word not merely into the names of individual mines but into their official company titles – Manvers Main Collieries Ltd or Houghton Main Colliery Co, for example.

One of the first mentions of the term had been as early as 1750 when Montagu Main opened at Scotswood, near Newcastle. Wynell's Main in North Wales dates back to 1753 and there are numerous other examples of relatively small mines bearing such titles, Measham Main in Leicestershire for instance, which was referred to as Main in some reference sources but not in others and is thought to have been so called to distinguish it from its smaller neighbour, Minorca Colliery, with which it shared a ventilation system and was under the same management in NCB days.

The smallest was probably Wagon Main, at Lowgates, near Staveley, which is thought to have been little more than a small drift mine.

The situation is made yet more complicated by the fact that many large coal seams bore the word 'Main' in their title, but there was not always a correlation between those and the names of the collieries on the surface. Ancient use of the word as a place name, Percy Main and Pelaw Main for example, could be related to the very early coal workings in those areas or could have emanated from the word Demesne (pronounced De-Main), which means 'all the land, not necessarily contiguous to the manor house, which was retained by a lord of the manor'.

The prime cause of confusion over the decades has been the large number of company takeovers that have taken place since the dawn of commercial coal mining. Some incoming owners would change the name of the colliery to prevent it clashing with their own 'main' pit, while others would retain the title, especially if it was well-known and highly regarded as a commercial coal product in the local area. This resulted in some companies owning more than one 'main' mine.

Following nationalisation in 1947, the need for one-upmanship between competing companies disappeared, but the National Coal Board took the view that it was not worth the effort and expense of changing all the registration documents, signs, stationery and suchlike, and so decided to retain most of the original titles. It wasn't until the 1980s that it finally decided to drop most of the suffixes, with the exception of Yorkshire's Markham Main, which was retained to avoid confusion with Markham Colliery in neighbouring Derbyshire. There had also been a Markham Colliery in South Wales.

By far the majority of 'Mains' were in South Yorkshire, and at one point the town of Doncaster had been virtually ringed by them.

● A similar marketing ploy was occasionally used in the crowded South Wales market in private owner days when some companies added the popular word 'Rhondda' or 'Merthyr' to the end of their colliery title even though they were not in Merthyr or the Rhondda! Examples were Lewis Merthyr, in Trehafod, and Duffryn Rhondda in the Afan Valley. Several other South Wales collieries included the word 'Navigation' in their title – a reference to the supply of coal to steam ships in the Victorian and Edwardian periods.

ABOVE: A colourful scene among the rosebay willowherb at Yorkshire's Clayton West Colliery as British Rail Class 37 No. 37040 shunts coal wagons on a hot August 5, 1977. This location is now the site of the narrow gauge Kirklees Light Railway. GAVIN MORRISON

gradually began to reverse, with more and more coal being imported.

The National Coal Board's name was altered to British Coal in January 1987. The revamp was designed to give a modern look to reflect the streamlined, slimmed-down industry but apart from a wholesale replacement of signage outside colliery buildings and some increased private sector involvement, the organisation remained basically the same.

Looking back on the NCB/British Coal era, there is no doubt that the company brought great benefits to the mining industry as a whole, but it had to take many unpalatable decisions in order to run the business efficiently and profitably. Some of those were seen by the miners and by the public at the time as wasteful - on a par with the worst excesses of British Rail, which in the 1960s began scrapping not only old obsolete locos but perfectly good ones that had been built at huge cost only five or six years earlier.

The BR controversy was caused by a decision to withdraw steam rapidly to meet an arbitrary deadline and a parallel can be drawn in the coal industry in the rush to close and demolish worked-out or inefficient pits, some of which were relatively new. The Robens era decisions included mines such as Redbrook, South

Yorkshire, which had cost £29million to rebuild in the early 1980s and whose new structures opened in 1985. It was condemned just 24 *months* later. Neighbouring Woolley Colliery, which had even more spent on it – £116million – was also knocked down despite its mid-1980s refurbishment.

"British Coal and the Government are not interested in whether collieries can produce coal efficiently or cheaply," stormed Barnsley Central MP Eric Illsley in 1987. "They are simply closing mines as part of a short-sighted strategy to reduce costs as quickly as possible." ▶

ABOVE: Sending coal by sea from coastal collieries in the North East dates back many centuries and the tradition was still being practised when this picture was taken in May 1985. BR diesel shunter No. 08747 gingerly edges towards the end of the loading staithes at Blyth with a load destined for the Danish collier *Jylland*. COLOUR-RAIL

ABOVE: Heading for the pithead baths, miners leave both levels of the shaft cage simultaneously at Desford Colliery, west of Leicester, in this NCB photo. Note how the men are handing their brass checks to the banksmen standing on the left at both levels.

ABOVE AND BELOW: The transition from NCB to British Coal – basically a name change only – took place in 1987 and saw the signage modified at all mines. Top: the old order at Maerdy Colliery in 1985 (note use of the Anglicised spelling) and (lower) the new look at Annesley Colliery in 1993. ABOVE: NICK PIGOTT; BELOW: ROBIN STEWART-SMITH

He blamed the situation on a Government decision to impose capital charges on individual collieries - charges and financial targets they simply could not meet on their own.

In the interests of fairness, former NCB/British Coal managers point out that many of the older collieries were genuine long-term loss-makers and would have closed eventually anyway, regardless of union activity. The board also encountered difficulties trying to manage at a time of restrictive workplace practices and carried massive liabilities in terms of pension fund and subsidence claim settlements - but there were nevertheless examples of 'creative accounting' that turned economic pits into uneconomic ones almost overnight: in one classic mid-1980s case in Yorkshire, construction of a coal preparation plant was supposed to have its £106million cost spread across a dozen mines in the area, but the rapid closure of nine of those pits suddenly meant the full cost being borne by the remaining three. Unsurprisingly, that put their paper accounts into the red - providing justification for closure.

Once natural gas joined the list of competitors and new houses were built with central heating systems instead of fireplaces, the NCB accepted that the domestic market was as good as lost and began to concentrate on power station supply. Electricity became known as 'coal by wire'.

In 1992, the Government (by then under the control of Conservative Prime Minister John Major) decided to implement a privatisation programme similar to the one it had announced for the railway industry. The remaining unprofitable pits would be shown no mercy so that those offered for sale would be attractive to private investors.

The announcement was made in the Commons by Cabinet Minister Michael Heseltine, who said he felt 'pain' over the proposed closure of 31 collieries. This prompted an ex-miner to write to the *Barnsley Chronicle* stating: "It's not pain but guilt. Pain is when a mother is told that her husband, son or father is dead in a pit disaster or when a wife is

ABOVE: Moving with the times: An artist's impression of Coal House, the NCB's new divisional headquarters at Doncaster, which opened in the mid-1960s.

ABOVE: It seems odd now to think that some of the more antiquated coal mines remained in operation long enough to be served by British Rail's smart new Class 60s, which weren't fully introduced until the 1990s. This is BR Coal Sector-allocated No. 60057 *Adam Smith* at Bolsover Colliery on February 23, 1993. NICK PIGOTT

told her husband is in hospital and will never be the same again."

By the time British Coal was sold off at the end of 1994, a mere 16 deep mines remained in the whole of the UK and the total number of miners was down to a paltry 7,000, compared with 1.2million in the 1920s.

Privatisation became reality with the passing of the Coal Industry Act 1994 and the administrative functions of British Coal were transferred to a new body, the Coal Authority, based in the Nottinghamshire mining town of Mansfield. The mines were handed to private ownership in January 1995,

although the need to clear up some of the remnants meant that British Coal wasn't officially wound up until January 26, 1997.

RJB Mining, owned by industrialist Richard Budge, paid £815million to buy the majority of the pits (including Asfordby, Thorne, the Selby complex ▶

BELOW: Snowdown Colliery, one of the principal mines in the isolated Kent coalfield, was one of the deepest and also one of the hottest in the country (see page 68). Note how it featured a mixture of conventional and friction-style headgear in this photograph taken before its 1987 closure. NICK PIGOTT

ABOVE: Many coal mines in the post-war era grew to enormous sizes and covered areas almost as great as small villages. This is a section of the extensive surface complex at Welbeck Colliery, north Nottinghamshire. ROBIN STEWART-SMITH

and 14 opencast sites). Tower Colliery, the last deep mine in South Wales, was bought by an employee buy-out team, Celtic Energy took nine opencast sites in Wales and a company called Midland Mining acquired Annesley Colliery and

applied for a licence to mine under Newstead Abbey. The application was refused after complaints from all over the world!

The £815m paid by RJB was the value of the surface assets only –

nothing was paid for the underground plant. Some of Budge's fellow directors were property speculators and very little allowance was made for mining development, leading to claims that the mines were being bought for short-term exploitation of reserves rather than for long-term investment.

Certainly, the new owners did not possess the financial clout of the NCB and many of the mines were closed over the next few years once they ceased to make a profit or encountered geological problems. The casualties included the virtually brand new mines at Selby and Asfordby, but for the few that were retained, substantial sums were spent on modernisation, automation and the driving of new underground roadways to open up fresh coalfaces. Collieries that benefited from such investment included Maltby, Kellingley, Daw Mill and Harworth, which had a new winding tower constructed as recently as 1996.

Roof bolts had been in use in America and Australia for several years but weren't adopted on a widescale basis in Britain until the late 1980s. They were 70% cheaper than the traditional arch method and enabled roadways to be built much faster. Harworth (where RJB also had its headquarters) broke a world record in the mid-1990s by driving through a mile of solid rock in just 24 weeks, but such development

ABOVE: The natural synergy between the coal and rail industries in the days when both were under state ownership resulted in mutually beneficial ventures such as the naming of main line locomotives after collieries. BR Coal Sector Class 58 No. 58046 stands at Thoresby during its naming ceremony on June 29, 1991. ROBIN STEWART-SMITH

work required vast sums of capital. In the nationalised era, the NCB could arrange for neighbouring collieries to increase production while an adjacent pit was shut for modernisation or redevelopment. The new private companies didn't have enough mines to be able to do that and so had to ask for Government subsidies.

Richard Budge left RJB Mining in 2001 and the company was subsequently renamed UK Coal. Budge went on to form a company called Coalpower, which bought Hatfield Colliery, near Doncaster.

Modernisation and automation highlights aside, the first decade of the new millennium saw total deep mine coal production fall to fewer than 10m tonnes a year... meaning that it was overtaken by the nation's opencast mines for the first time ever.

UK Coal soldiered on and as recently as 2013 wanted to open up new faces at its Daw Mill, Thoresby and Kellingley mines, but a huge underground fire at Daw Mill resulted in premature closure of that pit that year and when the Government refused the company subsidies for development of the other two pits in 2015, saying they did not represent value for money compared with cheap imports, the deep mining industry was condemned.

The only other colliery to survive into 2015, Hatfield, had been owned by a miners' consortium but that too couldn't survive the drastic drop in world coal prices that resulted from

ABOVE: By the time this picture was taken in 2002, the UK coal-mining industry was involved in only one race – a race to the bottom. Prince of Wales Colliery dominated the skyline of Pontefract racecourse in those days but was closed later that year and has since been demolished. PRESS ASSOCIATION

the dumping of cheap Chinese coal on to the international market. It closed suddenly in the summer of 2015 and has already been partly knocked down, although its headstocks and winding house were saved by a preservation order just 24 hours before they were due to be demolished.

Kellingley Colliery lifted its last piece of coal on December 18, 2015. So only imported and opencast supplies are now available to help the other forms of energy - biomass, gas, wind, solar, fracking, oil and nuclear - in the constant quest for cheap, safe, reliable electricity generation in Britain. ●

BELOW: The 'blues': We end this chapter with a 2016 photograph showing that the decline in the world of coal shows no sign of abating even though all the operational deep mines have now closed. This is Haig Colliery at Whitehaven, Cumbria, which until this year was preserved and open to the public – but it called it a day as a museum in January, just six months after closure of Leicestershire's Snibston mining museum. A picture of Haig in its prime can be seen on page 3. NICK PIGOTT

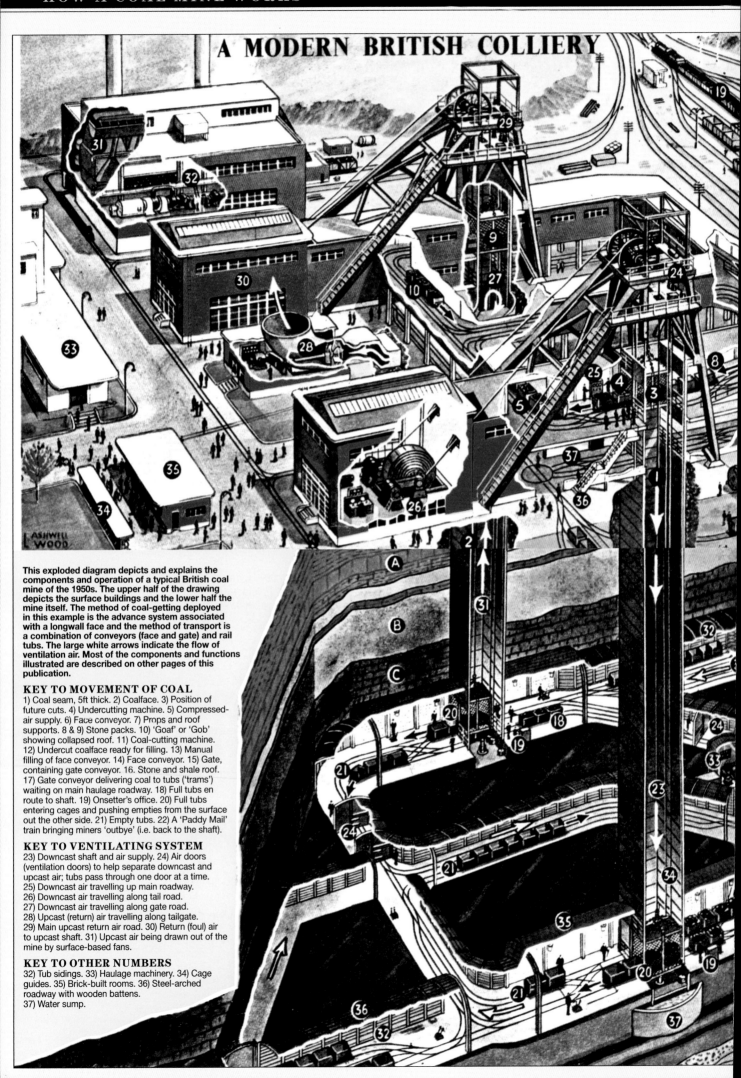

A MODERN BRITISH COLLIERY

This exploded diagram depicts and explains the components and operation of a typical British coal mine of the 1950s. The upper half of the drawing depicts the surface buildings and the lower half the mine itself. The method of coal-getting deployed in this example is the advance system associated with a longwall face and the method of transport is a combination of conveyors (face and gate) and rail tubs. The large white arrows indicate the flow of ventilation air. Most of the components and functions illustrated are described on other pages of this publication.

KEY TO MOVEMENT OF COAL

1) Coal seam, 5ft thick. 2) Coalface. 3) Position of future cuts. 4) Undercutting machine. 5) Compressed-air supply. 6) Face conveyor. 7) Props and roof supports. 8 & 9) Stone packs. 10) 'Goaf' or 'Gob' showing collapsed roof. 11) Coal-cutting machine. 12) Undercut coalface ready for filling. 13) Manual filling of face conveyor. 14) Face conveyor. 15) Gate, containing gate conveyor. 16. Stone and shale roof. 17) Gate conveyor delivering coal to tubs ('trams') waiting on main haulage roadway. 18) Full tubs en route to shaft. 19) Onsetter's office. 20) Full tubs entering cages and pushing empties from the surface out the other side. 21) Empty tubs. 22) A 'Paddy Mail' train bringing miners 'outbye' (i.e. back to the shaft).

KEY TO VENTILATING SYSTEM

23) Downcast shaft and air supply. 24) Air doors (ventilation doors) to help separate downcast and upcast air; tubs pass through one door at a time. 25) Downcast air travelling up main roadway. 26) Downcast air travelling along tail road. 27) Downcast air travelling along gate road. 28) Upcast (return) air travelling along tailgate. 29) Main upcast return air road. 30) Return (foul) air to upcast shaft. 31) Upcast air being drawn out of the mine by surface-based fans.

KEY TO OTHER NUMBERS

32) Tub sidings. 33) Haulage machinery. 34) Cage guides. 35) Brick-built rooms. 36) Steel-arched roadway with wooden battens. 37) Water sump.

KEY TO SURFACE STRUCTURES AND OPERATIONS

1) Downcast shaft. 2) Upcast shaft. 3) Cage in raised position. 4) Full tubs ('trams') being pushed out of cage by empties. 5) Tubs gravitate towards screen building. 6) Weighbridge. 7) Tippler. 8) Empty tubs hauled back to cage by cable. 9) Cage in upcast shaft. 10) Full tubs on way to screens. 11) Tippler. 12) Empty tubs returning to shaft. 13) Conveyor belt for sizing large coal and picking out stone, shale, slate etc. 14) Ditto for 'cobbles'. 15) Ditto for 'nuts'. 16) Ditto for 'smalls', which go straight to the washery. 17) Conveyor to rail-loading hopper. 18) Railway wagons. 19) Loaded train awaiting departure. 20) Smalls washery (coal preparation plant) with water/clarifier tower. 21) Washed smalls hopper to wagons. 22) Aerial ropeway for waste to spoil heap. 23) Spoil heap. 24) Downcast shaft headgear. 25) Banksman's office. 26) Winding drum, electric motor and control desk. 27) Ventilation tunnel from upcast shaft. 28) Fan house and evasse. 29) Upcast shaft headgear. 30) Upcast winding house. 31) Boiler house. 32) Power house, containing air-compressors, pumps and turbo-generators. 33) Pithead baths and canteen. 34) Cycle store. 35) Lamp room and medical centre. 36) Steps up to cage. 37) Tub maintenance dept. 38) Workshops. 39) Through roads. 40) Screen loading roads. 41) Sidings to stores and crippled wagons.

KEY TO GEOLOGICAL STRATA OF EARTH'S CRUST (at this mine):

A) Blue clay. B) Sand. C) Sandstone. D) Coal seams, between stone and shale. E) Millstone grit. F) Limestone. G) Old Red Sandstone.

ILLUSTRATION COURTESY ORION

THE UPS AND DO

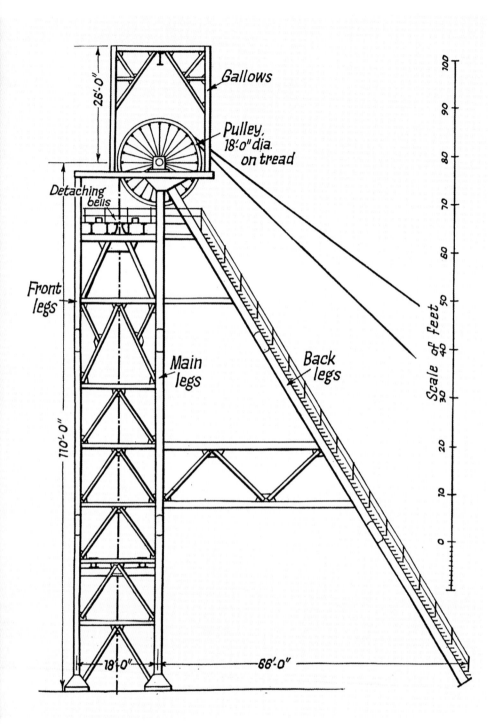

Gallows

Pulley,
18'-0" dia.
on tread

Detaching
bells

Front
legs

Main
legs

Back
legs

26'-0"

110'-0"

18'-0"

66'-0"

Scale of feet

THE internationally recognised symbol of coal mining is the winding tower, also known as the headstock, headgear or headframe. Topped by huge spoked pulley wheels called sheaves, they were used for winding coal, men and materials up and down the shafts.

Before the 1800s, headstocks were constructed of timber, having evolved from the rudimentary windlasses erected over the shallow shafts of bellpits, but as shafts became deeper and loads heavier, the height and strength of the gear had to increase too.

Deep mines of the type we are familiar with today began to appear in the late 18th century once the problem of water pumping had been overcome. Until then, shafts had rarely descended more than 300ft, but by 1801, a depth of 993ft had been achieved at Howgill Colliery on the Cumberland coast.

As technology improved, it was possible to sink shafts to depths of more than 3,000ft, below which inclined roadways could be driven down to give some modern collieries in Britain working depths of about 4,000ft. To put that into context, the deepest part of

the entire London Underground system is a mere 220ft.

There were several types of headstock over the years, with some of the modern 'Koepe' designs built for the NCB's superpits in the 1950s and '60s bearing more resemblance to concrete blocks of flats than to traditional steel towers.

Headstocks were either 'upcast' or 'downcast' types, depending on which direction the subterranean ventilation air passed through them. With the 'Koepe' towers there was little external difference between the two types, but with the steel-frame designs, it was usually easy to tell which was the upcast as it was normally clad in some form of shuttering - wood in the early days but more usually concrete or metal in later years. This was primarily so that fresh air entering the mine via the downcast shaft would not take the route of least resistance and come straight back up to the surface via the upcast without first passing through the underground network. (As explained in a previous chapter, air doors in the roadways also helped direct the air to where it was needed).

Before any new shaft could be sunk, numerous bore holes would be made all around the surface in order to provide surveyors with a 'picture' of the underground bed and seams - the purpose being that faults and folds in the earth's structure could give a misleading picture and lead to the shaft (or perhaps even the entire mine) being an expensive folly.

To make a test bore hole for a typical modern deep mine, a hollow cylindrical drill with a diamond-tipped or saw-toothed bit would be progressively driven into the ground by machine with additional sections continuously screwed on to it at the top until the desired depth was reached. Cores or 'plugs' of earth, rock and coal entered the hollow cylinder sections, were brought to the surface and then laid end-to-end on the ground for analysis by geologists.

Once the decision to go ahead was taken, a specialist team of shaft-sinkers would be brought in to dig into the soft overburden and sub-soils. A temporary headstock would then be erected above the cavity for lowering and raising muck and materials. A platform containing items of equipment and a huge bucket known as a 'hoppit' were also used by the sinkers, who would ride in the hoppit themselves.

As they worked their way down through the various strata, the sinkers would encounter varying volumes of water from subterranean aquifers, which would have to be pumped out as

ABOVE: Shaft-sinkers were a breed apart, usually employed on a contractual basis and travelling from coalfield to coalfield as new mines were opened across the country. Note the waterproof over-garments and special headgear designed to deflect the water that cascaded down the shafts.

ABOVE: One of the largest and most extraordinary mines in terms of headgear variety was Chatterley Whitfield, in Staffordshire, which ended its days with no fewer than four winding towers, each of a different design - three of which are shown here. Fortunately, the colliery has been preserved, albeit in an increasingly decrepit state. NICK PIGOTT

they progressed. This could vary from a highly manageable 20 gallons a minute to a fast-flowing torrent of several thousand gallons a minute. Assuming they could maintain the flow, the sinkers would insert cast-iron bolted segments known as 'tubbing' into the shaft to form a watertight seal. In the 20th century, this process was sped up by technological improvements such as cementation or even temporarily freezing the ground around the shaft.

This they would do by bringing in a surface-based refrigeration plant to 'freeze-dry' the rock, soil and sand long enough for the waterproofed shaft linings to be installed and secured. The system worked by cooling brine to below the freezing point of water and then injecting it into the ground to form walls of ice around the shaft. Once the tubbing had been inserted, the refrigeration plant could be switched off.

▶

ABOVE AND LEFT: In the 19th and early 20th centuries, many winding towers were of the tandem variety. This set at Brinsley Colliery, near Eastwood, was built in 1872 and survived the pit's 1934 closure in order to provide access to neighbouring pits. By the time it came out of service in 1970, its historic importance was recognised and it was taken to the National Mining Museum, which at that time was based at Lound Hall, near Retford. When the museum vacated those premises, it was returned to Brinsley and re-erected as a monument in the early 1990s.

ABOVE: Timber-clad temporary structures erected by shaft-sinkers at Vane Tempest Colliery in County Durham.

RIGHT: Pit banks of downcast shifts were hives of activity when miners entered or left the cages, but between shifts they were often much quieter than the constantly busy coal-raising upcast shafts. This was Kellingley's downcast pit bank.

ABOVE: An unusual view up through the superstructure of a winding tower from the cage entrance and showing the multiple rope system required to operate a shaft with two cages. This example is at Blaenafon Colliery, which utilises a drift as its other means of exit. NICK PIGOTT

RIGHT: The view down into a shaft a few days after the sinkers had started work. Water ingress was a common problem, but from the late 1950s onwards, mechanical 'cactus' grabs began to be used, which sped up the task considerably.

Depending on the surrounding ground conditions, the permanent lining would normally be formed either with bricks, concrete blocks or by pouring concrete behind reinforced shuttering. Where bricks were used, a kerb-ring would be placed around the shaft wall on which to lay the bricks. Once the cement had set, the kerb-ring

would be lowered about three feet and another set of bricks laid.

Once the 'rockhead' was reached, explosives had to be used to enable sinking to continue. The blasting was undertaken in stages; holes would be drilled for the charges, all equipment would be sent to the surface to protect it, and the men would exit the shaft

themselves. They would then detonate the charges remotely before re-entering the shaft to remove the broken rock.

Before the invention of remote-controlled devices, the shotfirer had to remain in the shaft long enough to light a very long fuse before clambering into the hoppit and being hoisted quickly to the surface. You found out who your mates were in situations like that!

This procedure would be repeated hundreds of times over a period of months or years until the desired depth was attained. In the case of some collieries, it could take as long as three years before the first seam of coal was even located, although the introduction of high-capacity 'cactus' grabs in the 1960s sped the process up.

DID YOU **KNOW?**

When the pithead baths at Chatterley-Whitfield were opened in 1938, miners had to pay 6d a week to use them and still had to take their own soap and towel. It wasn't until the NCB took over in 1947 that they were made free.

As the shaft grew deeper, fresh air would have to be sent down to the men using a surface fan and canvas ducts or tubes to prevent the air becoming stale.

Once completed and fully lined, permanent headgear would be constructed on the surface to enable the mine developers and their equipment to go down in cages and begin developing the haulage roads that would access the various coal seams. A large pillar of unworked coal would always be left at the base of the shafts to ensure their long-term stability. Since 1862, all British mines have had to have a minimum of two linked shafts (or other means of egress such as a drift) for emergency escape purposes.

Any item of machinery that was too large to fit into the cage would either be dismantled first or (in the case of long locomotives and suchlike) suspended vertically from the underside of the cage and then brought round to the horizontal at the bottom for off-loading. That explains why so many locomotives and other large forms of equipment were abandoned in the seams upon closure of a mine.

Shafts weren't just used for bringing up coal, moving men and materials and providing ventilation; to their sides were also fitted pipes for water and compressed air, cables for electricity and wires for telephones and other means of communication.

ABOVE: The headgear of Kiveton Park Colliery lay alongside the Worksop-Sheffield main passenger line. The colliery was one of the last in the Sheffield area to close and is seen here on September 29, 1994 with Class 58 No.58036 preparing to depart with a loaded Merry-go-Round train. GAVIN MORRISON

Shaft collars (also known as banks) often had sloping surrounds so that rain and other liquids would run away from them, but water and sludge nevertheless accumulated in a sump at the foot of the shaft and had to be frequently removed.

In operation, a system of bell codes or hooter sounds were used by banksmen, onsetters and winding enginemen to signal when cages were ready to be raised or lowered, or when the lower half of a double-decker cage needed manoeuvring up or down.

The speeds at which the cages could be wound could reach 90ft per second (about 60mph) and it was sometimes necessary for shafts to be widened at the halfway point to reduce the air pressure when two cages passed each ▶

BELOW: The collection of buildings around the base of a winding tower is collectively known as the heapstead and the most impressive and solidly built survivor can be found at Pleasley Colliery, near Mansfield. The museum there houses an impressive collection of mining memorabilia, two beautifully maintained steam winding engines, a brace of headstocks and a tall smokestack. NICK PIGOTT

ABOVE: This most remarkable photograph depicts the operation to replace an old headstock with a new one at Harworth Colliery in 1996. To prevent the shaft being out of action too long, the new one was erected alongside and slid in on rails after demolition of the old one. PRESS ASSOCIATION

Modern shafts were up to 30ft diameter and capable of taking 20-ton skips or cages containing as many as 100 men at a time, but many as small as 8ft diameter remained in use into the 1960s. At busy collieries, the coal-winding engines would run virtually non-stop 24 hours a day.

The vast majority of UK shafts were equipped with two cages or skips secured to separate ropes. To enable men to ride in a skip-winding shaft in an emergency, it was possible for an auxiliary cage to be mounted above a skip.

Before the 20th century, most headframes were made of timber - usually oak or pitch pine - and erected in a tandem arrangement with two narrow shafts sharing a set of ropes, but if anything happened to the rope or winding engine, both shafts would be out of action and there would be no escape, so newer collieries were built with separate shafts, each with its own winder. After the Hartley Colliery disaster of 1862, in which the cast-iron beam of the mine's pumping engine snapped and fell down the shaft, trapping 204 men - all of whom died - an Act of Parliament was passed requiring all collieries with more than 30 men underground at the same time to have two separate shafts or means of escape. Hartley had possessed one shaft separated into two compartments by a wooden brattice.

other at speed in the same shaft. The sheaves at the top of each headgear rotated in opposite directions as the winding ropes passed over them.

Without exception, a group of miners interviewed in the 1990s agreed that their very first trip to the pit bottom had been terrifying. Said one: "As soon as the gate was clanged shut on the cage and the banksman stood back and rang the signal, we dropped like a stone. About half way down, your ears suddenly went as though you were deaf and it seemed as though you were coming back to the top. But then I saw a light flash by and realised we were still going down. I was frightened to death."

Skip Winding

Skip-winding was introduced in modern mines to increase the volume and frequency of coal-raising in association with underground and surface conveyor belts. Before then, rail-borne tubs had to be laboriously conveyed to the surface in cages and sent down again when empty.

LEFT: This example of a coal-raising/man-riding skip is on display at Caphouse Colliery Museum.

RIGHT: Diagram showing how the skip system works.

BELOW: A rare photograph taken at the top of a coal-raising shaft while in full operation. The freshly mined coal has just been deposited from the skip and is starting its journey to the preparation plant via inclined conveyors as automatic water vapour jets suppress the coal dust. This now-historic scene was photographed with permission at Kellingley Colliery on November 25, 2015. NICK PIGOTT

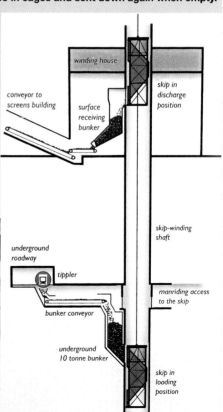

RIGHT: Among the largest and most impressive examples of headgear in Britain were the two huge towers that once dominated the scene at Lea Hall Colliery, Staffordshire. Opened by the NCB in 1960, the towers incorporated ground-mounted Koepe systems with four pulleys each and produced coal for Rugeley power station, which adjoined it. The power station is due to close this summer and the colliery has been replaced by a huge distribution centre for the Amazon online retail firm. In this May 1989 photo, one of the towers dwarfs Hunslet surface shunter No. 8825. GORDON EDGAR

The Coal Mines Act of 1911 decreed that new mines employing more than 30 pcoplc had to have headframes built of non-inflammable materials. That led to a rapid increase in the lattice girder (and later rolled steel) types that became so familiar in the coalfields of Britain. Some pitch pine headgears nevertheless remained in use well into the 1950s.

Headstocks were built in dozens of different shapes and sizes but in later years were basically of two main types: The traditional steel winding tower contained two sheave pulley wheels linked by cables to a separate winding house on the surface (one house for each tower). The cable drums within the winding house were operated by large stationary steam engines in the early years and then by electricity and were manned by a skilled driver who normally had to work in isolation so that he would not be distracted by conversation or events going on around him. Safety devices were improved over the years, but total concentration was necessary to prevent the risk of a fatal over-wind (see Accidents chapter on page 90).

The second type of headgear was generally known as the Koepe friction-winding type and was installed at many of the new or refurbished superpits in the National Coal Board era. The system did not use a conventional winding drum but instead utilised the weight of the ropes, cagcs and skips to assist the grip of the ropes on the sheave wheels. The cages were secured to opposite ends of the same single (or multiple) rope, which was then passed over surge pads on a smaller drum, the drive being transmitted to the rope(s).

In a modern Koepe headstock, the sheave wheels (which included a deflecting pulley) were not usually visible but were enclosed in concrete or metal cladding. The reason is that the electric winding engine and controller's cabin were usually located at the top of the tower, rather than being in an adjacent building (although there were some examples of ground-mounted Koepe winders too). Friction hoists required up to 30% less power and space to work and were named after their German inventor, Friederich Koepe.

A third and older type of winding tower, examples of which were

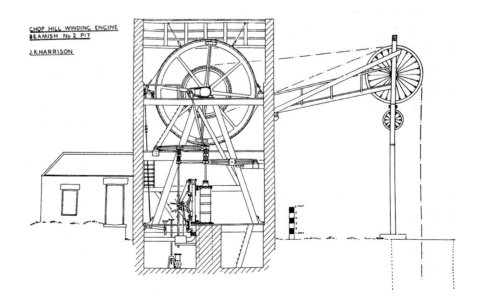

ABOVE: A type of headstock found in County Durham but very rarely elsewhere was the vertical-cylinder winding engine, which used a steam-powered lever system to rotate a flywheel, which in turn worked a shaft pulley sheave via ropes. The last working example of this Victorian design can be seen in operation at Beamish Colliery (see page 126). PICTURE: BEAMISH MUSEUM ▶

ABOVE: Bestwood Colliery was once a huge sprawling industrial complex. Today all that remains is the headgear, winding house and a small building surrounded by neat lawns in a country park, but it nevertheless makes for a friendly and interesting visit. NICK PIGOTT

MIDDLE: The only headstock in Britain still used for its original purpose of lowering people underground in an authentic shaft and cage on an everyday basis is at Big Pit Colliery in Blaenafon – home of the Welsh National Coal Museum. A few pulley wheels at other mines are still operational but either not linked to a shaft or not used every day. In this view can be seen two ex-NCB locos, a Hudswell Clarke 0-6-0ST and a Barclay 0-4-0ST. NICK PIGOTT

prevalent in the Great Northern Coalfield, was known as the lever-type vertical winding engine. Patented by Newcastle engineer Phileas Crowther in 1800, it utilised a vertical steam cylinder to drive a large flywheel above it, which in turn drove the shaft pulley wheel by rope. This negated the need for a separate horizontal-cylindered engine in a separate building, but the concept didn't spread much beyond County Durham. Half a dozen engines of this type were still in operation in the mid-1950s and one is preserved in working order at Beamish.

There was a fourth type - the water-balanced winder - which was popular in relatively shallow collieries, especially in South Wales. The cages were fitted with water tanks beneath their floors. At the top, water would be let into the tank and the weight would cause that cage (containing an empty tub or tram) to descend while the cage in the other shaft, whose water tank had been emptied at the bottom, would ascend with a full load.

With such a huge number of collieries in Britain, it was inevitable that there would be exceptions and permutations to the types of winding

gear. For example, one of the large modern shafts at Hem Heath Colliery, near Stoke-on-Trent, had two winders in one shaft - a standard electric winder on one side, operating down to the 612yd level, as well as a ground-mounted Koepe electric winder operating down to the 1,062yd level. Another Staffordshire colliery, Lea Hall, had a German-inspired twin headgear set with four sheave wheels serving two shafts on each of its two huge 'A'-frame structures. The 200ft high headstocks of Nottinghamshire's Clipstone Colliery, also of German design, were at the time

ABOVE: A water-balanced headstock preserved at Big Pit, Blaenafon, and (left), a diagram explaining how such winding gear functioned.

ABOVE: The preserved headstock at Astley Green Colliery in Lancashire is arguably the most striking lattice steel example left in Britain. Standing 98ft tall, it is the last survivor in a coalfield once chock-full of collieries. The winding house and its unique twin tandem compound steam engine have also survived and are part of Astley Green Colliery Museum. NICK PIGOTT

of their construction in 1953 the tallest in Europe.

Most collieries had a minimum of two winding towers – an upcast and a downcast, but some large mines had as many as five or six separate sets of headgear on one site, depending on how many underground seams were being worked. Some smaller mines had only one winding tower, but in those cases

there would either be a drift or a fan shaft on the premises as well.

Preservation has left us with several examples of steel headframes in the UK but at the time of writing, only three examples of the tower-

mounted Koepe type survive following demolition of one at Harworth on April 11, 2016. Built as recently as 1989, it bit the dust after defying an attempt to knock it down with explosives the day before. ●

BELOW: One of the most controversial closures of a colliery in 2015 was not even an operational mine! Leicestershire County Council axed the well-equipped Snibston Discovery Centre, one of the county's best-known tourist attractions. The colliery itself - which has a very rare tandem headstock in addition to a conventional winding tower - can trace its ancestry back to the days of George Stephenson and will survive… but it has been closed to the public. NICK PIGOTT

A Colliery **Gallery**

To round off this chapter, we present a gallery of photographs showing the wide architectural variety of colliery headstocks in Britain.
PICTURES BY NICK PIGOTT UNLESS STATED.

ABOVE: The tallest headstock in the UK until its 2016 demolition was the Koepe winding tower at Harworth Colliery, south of Doncaster. This 220ft high structure had been constructed as recently as 1989 and had clearly been built to last, for it defied attempts to demolish it by explosives and had to be toppled by manual means on April 11. NICK PIGOTT

ABOVE MIDDLE: The large 'A' in this picture stood for Annesley, a major colliery that survived into the 21st century but has since been turned into a housing estate.

ABOVE: A large 'A'-frame winding tower survives in splendid isolation on the site of Scotland's Barony Colliery, near Auchinleck in East Ayrshire. The bodies of four miners killed in a pit accident in 1962 lie beneath the tower. JOHN CULLEN

ABOVE: Tall towers – 1: Rossington Colliery in 2007. These handsome structures south-east of Doncaster have since been demolished. NICK PIGOTT

ABOVE: Many headstocks featured a metal or concrete frame above the sheaves. This was a frame hoist, also known as a gallows or gibbet, and was used whenever the pulleys or ropes needed changing. This example is at Lady Victoria Colliery in Scotland. In later years, several were removed as the height, reach and capacity of road-based mobile cranes increased.

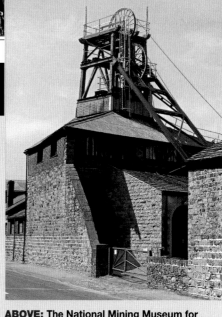

ABOVE: The National Mining Museum for England is based in the former Caphouse Colliery, near Wakefield, Yorkshire. Underground tours enhance the experience for visitors.

ABOVE: One of the smallest preserved headstocks in Britain is that of Foxfield Colliery at Dilhorne, near the end of the Foxfield Railway in Staffordshire. Built of concrete, it is one of two on the site, the other also being concrete but of taller and more conventional appearance.

ABOVE: Sad yet unbowed, the upcast tower of Tower Colliery – last deep mine in South Wales. It was closed by British Coal in 1994 but was bought by its workforce and continued to work until 2008 when it closed for the last time.

ABOVE: Tall towers – 2: Clipstone Colliery in 2015. These towers in north Nottinghamshire enjoy protected status and still stand, but for how long?

ABOVE: Arguably the most 'space-age' headstocks ever erected in Britain were those at the ill-fated Thorne Colliery, near Doncaster. They lasted only 25 years, from 1979 to 2004. NCB

'THE HARDEST WO

THE phrase 'working at the coalface' is known throughout the world as a reference to the core task in any operation, regardless of whether the business concerned is in heavy industry or merely office-based.

Few jobs carried such a globally respected reputation for hard work and high risk and few were surrounded by such mystique... for the vast majority of the world's inhabitants have never been down an operational mine and thus have only a vague impression of what conditions must have been like.

The nature of deep coalface work in Britain changed out of all recognition during the last few years of its existence, culminating in a well-lit and fully mechanised environment in many major collieries. A century and a half ago, it was, as Derbyshire miner William Wardle described it, "the hardest work under Heaven".

As some of the photographs and drawings in this publication show, coalface work between the 18th and mid-20th centuries could be horrendous. The seams were often extremely thin and after crawling along rough terrain in virtual pitch darkness for perhaps a mile or so to reach the face, the men would have to spend the whole shift on their knees or lying on their side in order to hew the coal with a hand-held pick.

Where high-quality coal for coking was required, some pits in the North East were still working seams of less than 2ft height as late as the 1960s. As a pan shovel was almost 2ft wide, this meant that a miner who accidentally took a shovel in the wrong way round would have to take it back to the gateroad just to turn it over!

In the worst situations, a collier would have to lie in two or three inches of foul black water that splashed over him every time he wielded his pick - all the time living in fear of a sharp piece of rock falling and slicing through his neck, waist or leg. Experienced colliers learnt to tell where and when falls were likely to occur, but even they were sometimes caught unawares by a sudden collapse.

Even if not killed outright by such a fall, their route to safety could be blocked by tons of rock or they would occasionally see a workmate killed just feet away and would have to live with the memory for the rest of their lives. There was no such thing as trauma counselling in those days!

Small wonder that psychological, lung, back and muscle complaints were rife, yet such men had no option but to carry on working as there was usually no sick pay.

Undercutting - also known in the old days as holing-out - was the means by which a thin slot had to be created at the base of the coalface in order to encourage the main body of coal above the slot to come crashing on to the floor ready for shovelling into tubs. Short wooden props known as sprags or nogs were used to hold the coal up during the holing-out process but, as can be imagined, it was an incredibly hazardous job. To make it worse, the miners had only cloth caps to protect their heads. Sadly, falls of coal were commonplace in the Victorian and early 20th century eras, frequently causing injury or death.

The greater use of ponies underground after 1842 helped ease conditions in some collieries as the

ABOVE: This illustration from the early 1920s shows what would be seen if it had been possible to remove the millions of tons of earth above a non-mechanised longwall coalface. It shows how the gate approaches the face at a right angle and how the goaf or 'gob' (the void created by the most recently hewn coal) is filled by hand with packs of stone and other waste to support the roof once the timber props are removed. This face was being worked by the advance method; in later years many mines would switch to the retreat method (see main text).

roadways had to have their height increased to enable the animals to walk, but the districts nearest the coalfaces themselves were often still very low.

To advance or retreat?: Originally, mining was carried out by the room & pillar (also known as pillar & stall) method, but in England towards the end of the 17th century, the concept of longwall mining was developed. Sometimes known as the 'Shropshire' method, it basically involved all the coal being taken from a single face, leaving a large void known as the 'goaf' or the 'gob' where it had been extracted. That space normally had to be packed with stone or timber props to prevent its total collapse, but there were basically two methods of longwall mining, known as Advance and Retreat.

In the first, coal-cutting would begin at the shaft or drift end of a new mine and advance into the coal deposits, with the lengths of the accompanying access roads keeping pace with the face as progress was made.

In the more modern method of retreat mining, the roads were built first and extended all the way to the far boundary of the district to be mined. Shorter roadways known as 'gates' were then driven off at right angles, one a main gate and the other a tail gate. The longwall coalface ran between the two gates, effectively isolating a large panel of coal that was then cut back towards the direction of the main roadway.

The retreat system had several advantages, the main one being that the void behind the face did not need to be supported beyond the section being cut at any particular moment and

ABOVE: To loosen the coal at the face in the early years of mechanisation, compressed-air tools were used to drill holes for explosive charges. It was safe to detonate such shot-firing charges as long as stringent tests had been made by an official beforehand to ensure no pockets of flammable methane gas were present.

could simply be allowed to collapse and be abandoned.

It had further benefits in that any geological problems or areas of spontaneous combustion could usually be identified before production began, thus minimising hold-ups and expensive mistakes. It was also much faster and more efficient once coal-cutting had started - but the driving

of complete roadways and gateways before any income could be earned from the coal required a major capital outlay and was therefore expensive.

For that reason, private owners post-1994 often required Government subsidy to develop new faces and when that subsidy dried up in the 21st century, the end of deep mining in the UK was inevitable.

The main gate of a longwall coalface would typically be the intake airway and the tail gate the return airway, carrying away the coal dust and gases. To reduce the risk of methane explosions, this end of the face normally contained the electrical ▶

ABOVE: In the early years, roadways had to be extended and roofs ripped with picks and shovels but the mechanised era brought compressed-air-driven 'road-header' machines, which used a rotary drill bit on the end of a movable arm to rip out the stone.

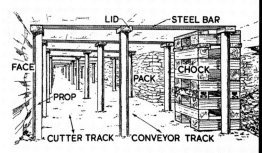

ABOVE: Seen in conjunction with the picture on the opposite page, this view along a traditional longwall coalface worked by the advance method shows the permanent pack and also a temporary chock made of timber beams to provide additional support to the roof while packs, props, lids and steel bars were being erected.

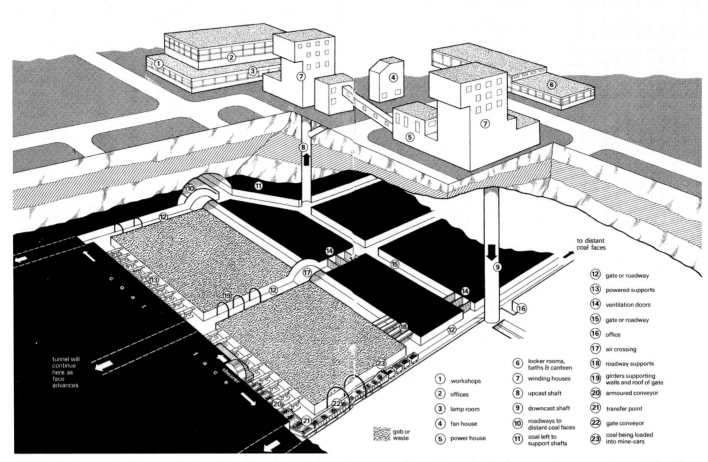

ABOVE: A cutaway view into a coal mine which, although relatively modern and partly mechanised with shearer and conveyors, is worked on the advance method with the coal taken to the shaft in mine cars. In later years, a trunk conveyor would replace the mine car transfer point and the coal would be raised to the surface in a skip rather than a cage.

Key (from diagram):

1. workshops
2. offices
3. lamp room
4. fan house
5. power house
6. locker rooms, baths & canteen
7. winding houses
8. upcast shaft
9. downcast shaft
10. roadways to distant coal faces
11. coal left to support shafts
12. gate or roadway
13. powered supports
14. ventilation doors
15. gate or roadway
16. office
17. air crossing
18. roadway supports
19. girders supporting walls and roof of gate
20. armoured conveyor
21. transfer point
22. gate conveyor
23. coal being loaded into mine-cars

gob or waste

to distant coal faces

tunnel will continue here as face advances

switchgear, hydraulic tanks and equipment necessary to power the cutter-loader and self-advancing roof supports.

The retreat method was developed in the late 19th century but didn't become widespread in Britain until the 20th due to the high initial costs.

Until the advent of steel archways and mechanised roof supports, all methods of mining required timber pit props in the roadways and at the face. Oak examples discovered in an old room & pillar mine at Coleorton, Leicestershire, have been carbon-dated to the 1400s, but most collieries used props made from Scottish or Norwegian spruce trees due to their combination of strength and elasticity.

The props and their timber caps created many thousands of miles of tunnels under Britain as a whole, yet the word 'tunnel' was rarely used in coal-mining parlance. The preferred terms were 'roadway', 'gate', 'heading', 'drivage' or 'haulage road', depending on size and usage.

Strictly speaking, a tunnel has to be open at both ends, but the word nevertheless occurs frequently in official mining

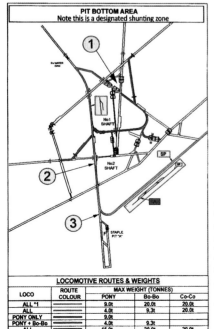

PIT BOTTOM AREA
Note this is a designated shunting zone

RIGHT: This is the official diagram used by UK Coal at its Thoresby Colliery in 2015 to show the extent to which the mine's roadways had extended. It is not to scale as the actual length depicted here was more than five miles long but it shows the gates leading to the most recent coalfaces (top right) and the rail tracks leading along the drifts from shaft bottom at lower left. It will be seen that the rail system around the shaft bottom area is surprisingly complex.

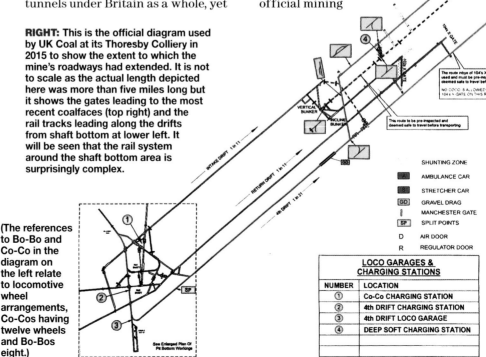

(The references to Bo-Bo and Co-Co in the diagram on the left relate to locomotive wheel arrangements, Co-Cos having twelve wheels and Bo-Bos eight.)

SHUNTING ZONE
AMBULANCE CAR
STRETCHER CAR
GRAVEL DRAG
MANCHESTER GATE
SPLIT POINTS
D   AIR DOOR
R   REGULATOR DOOR

LOCO GARAGES & CHARGING STATIONS	
NUMBER	LOCATION
1	Co-Co CHARGING STATION
2	4th DRIFT CHARGING STATION
3	4th DRIFT LOCO GARAGE
4	DEEP SOFT CHARGING STATION

LOCOMOTIVE ROUTES & WEIGHTS				
LOCO	ROUTE COLOUR	MAX WEIGHT (TONNES)		
		PONY	Bo-Bo	Co-Co
ALL *1		9.0t	20.0t	20.0t
ALL		4.0t	9.3t	20.0t
PONY ONLY		9.0t		
PONY + Bo-Bo		4.0t	9.3t	
ALL		15.0t	20.0t	20.0t

ABOVE: The coalfaces in Warwickshire were among the thickest in the country and this enabled Daw Mill Colliery to enjoy the rare luxury of a high, wide, well-lit roadway containing no fewer than three rail tracks. Such roadways were sometimes known by miners as 'motorways' but should more accurately have been called 'main lines'.

ABOVE: Even in the safest and most modern mines, reminders of the immense pressure being brought to bear on the roof were never far away. This picture was taken 2,200ft below the ground at Thoresby in 2015 and shows how metal arches in a roadway had buckled under the weight and how traditional timber props had been brought in to support the roof. NICK PIGOTT

the miners to lung problems and eye injuries due to the dust and shards thrown up from the rock and some took to wearing protective masks and goggles in later years.

In more recent times, the task of road building was speeded up by the introduction of roof bolt technology. Basically, a long hole of 8ft or more would be drilled into a newly ▶

documentation, especially when used as a verb, and some large roadways in modern mines were driven by cylindrical tunnel-boring machines in exactly the same way as railway tunnels are constructed, so there was a considerable terminology crossover between the two disciplines. Dawdon Colliery, in County Durham, was one mine in which a full-face tunnel-borer was deployed in the mid-1970s.

A roadway was known as such even if it had no space in it for anything other than rail tracks. In such cases, it would often be referred to as a 'locomotive road' because miners surprisingly didn't use the word 'railway' very often either, the other preferred terms being 'tub track', 'haulage road' or 'haulage way'.

Travel in the direction of a coalface was known as 'inbye' and travel back towards a shaft was referred to as 'outbye'.

In latter years, special road-header machines were built to rip out the stone but before that it had been a case of drilling, blasting and shovelling to construct a roadway. The men who did that were even more prone than

Geological Problems

THE dreaded term 'geological problems' could cover a multitude of sins (in fact, many miners considered it a euphemism deployed by owners as an excuse to close an otherwise sound pit). We shall never know now whether such cynicism was always justified, but many collieries did definitely suffer from serious instabilities – Hucknall No. 2 for example, which was struck by a sudden massive intrusion of sandstone in 1986.

The earth's crust is constantly restless and although roof falls were usually the result of insufficient prop support, the floor of a mine would often move too, being thrust upwards by tremendous forces of nature. In such cases, miners would have to restore them to a reasonably level state by a process of cutting and smoothing known as 'dinting'. In later years, special machines were devised to perform this function.

In some circumstances, usually at deeper depths, constant maintenance and repair of roadways was necessary as the weight and pressure of the strata surrounding them in some areas caused the roof arches to buckle, the ground to heave up and the height of the roadway to reduce. In areas prone to such pincer-like convergence, regular setting of new arches had to be factored in by colliery managers for it was not unknown for ground settlement to reduce the height of a thin seam from, say, 2ft to 18 inches over the course of a single weekend.

Due to prehistoric earth thrust, some seams were almost vertical and were known as edge seams or 'rearers'. In 1972, a seam of 1-in-2 (as steep as the roof of a house) was opened at Arkwright Colliery, Derbyshire, and required several special measures to enable men to work up and down it safely.

Geological problems could also mean strata faults. These could cause huge differences in seam depths, the Top Hard seam at Newstead Colliery, for instance, being located at 484 yards in No. 1 shaft but only at 426 yards in No. 2. Until the science of geology was better understood, major faults made coal-hewers in the Middle Ages believe mistakenly that they had found two different seams.

Faults have had a big bearing on the internal layouts of mines and have often dictated where shafts and roadways are built.

ABOVE: Coal seams affected by geological faulting can be sharply inclined, some almost vertically.

Flooding also fell under the heading of geological problems. Many mines, especially older ones whose shafts did not extend beneath the local water table, suffered terribly from fluid intrusion and had to have powerful pumps in continuous operation. Even after the merger of collieries for economic reasons in later years, otherwise-redundant shafts and headstocks would often be retained to pump water out of the combined workings.

As can be imagined, floods caused numerous tragedies over the years, the most recent in Britain occurring in 2011 with the loss of four lives. Some of the worst examples are dealt with on pages 90 to 95.

Why some mines were so hot

TEMPERATURES underground are dictated by the geothermal gradient, which rises by 1 degree Fahrenheit for every 70ft of depth (2.5 degrees Celsius for every 100 metres). On top of that, powerful machines create heat, the bodies of hard-working men add to it and the oxidation of strata also generates heat.

Trapping all that in a confined space explains why the temperature gets hotter nearer the coalface, and can reach 100F (38C). On a bitter winter's day, it could be very cold at the bottom of the downcast shaft, but sweltering at the face.

"Working at the coalface is like sweating in a sauna for six hours," said one Hatfield Colliery miner in 2012. "They do their best to get fresh air to you but you're half a mile beneath the ground so it's going to be hot."

"It's like being abroad when you first get off the plane," commented a Kellingley miner. "That sort of heat can make you quickly ill if you're not acclimatised and there can also be 98% humidity down there. They say it can take 10 years off your life."

The contrasts in temperature were also dramatic. Stepping through airlock doors from hot return air to cold intake air could reduce the temperature instantly from 90F to 30F.

Some hot mines with faces five miles or so from pit bottom had huge booster fans about halfway inbye in an effort to cool the air and keep it flowing in the required amounts.

Losing so much water through sweat and taking only modest amounts of food in his 'snap' tin meant that a miner didn't need to answer the call of nature as often as most people despite getting through several pints of drinking water per shift from the 'Dudley' canister carried in a leather pouch on his belt, but when he did… it was a case of just finding somewhere private in the abandoned workings!

Some of the hottest mines in the country were in Kent. Snowdown, despite its chilly-sounding name, was notorious and was known as 'the Inferno' because it was "hotter than Hell" 3,000ft below the earth's crust.

It is said of that and the other Kentish mines that even underpants were too hot to bear and that the tough face workers sometimes used to borrow their wives' briefs! Temperatures in the deepest mines could reach 100F, coupled with an almost unbearable humidity of almost 100%.

ABOVE: Photographic proof that miners in the hottest and deepest pits often had to strip down to their underwear in order to cope with the oppressive heat and humidity. This picture was taken at Tilmanstone Colliery in Kent.

ABOVE: Filling a large water bottle before going on shift was essential. Some could hold eight pints and were carried in a leather pouch on the miner's belt.

excavated roof or wall until it reached a strong layer of rock that could support its own weight. The hole was packed with fast-setting resin, a long bolt was driven in by a special machine and then tightened to pull and bind the whole lot together. Heavy-duty netting was used in conjunction with the bolts to catch any small bits of rock that might break away from the outer layer of the roof. Roof bolts were much quicker to fit and enabled roadways to be made much higher and wider than would previously have been the case. Transport of bolts and resins was also much easier than had been the case with the bulkier steel arch girders.

Another development was known as 'horizon' mining. The traditional method was to follow the undulations of the coal seam via the underground roadways, but that often caused severe gradients, making transport along them difficult. The roadways also required

constant maintenance to counter the crushing effect of having been constructed through the area from which the mineral had been extracted.

With horizon mining, level roadways (hence the name horizon) were driven from the shafts to the extremity of the area to be mined and were designed to intersect the maximum number of seams as often as possible. At the points of intersection, short headings were driven up or down into the seam to extract the coal. As with retreat mining, a major capital outlay was required, but the advantages outweighed this once production began as much longer trainloads could be taken to the shaft.

The NCB laid horizon lines in some of its new superpits during the early years of underground rail haulage of coal, but construction of the systems produced vast quantities of waste rock and they were in any case really only suited to large areas of virgin coal

in new mines. There became less call for them as conveyor technology and capacity improved.

British mines were typically divided up into underground areas known as districts and miners working in quiet, or worked-out, districts, would sometimes report being able to hear the machinery of a nearby colliery working at a level above or below them. Overlapping of roadways had been going on since the very earliest years of coal mining, with the difference being that in the old days, they often weren't aware that neighbouring workings existed. There is a report of an Edwardian-era collier who suddenly fell through into a gallery that had been abandoned almost a century earlier and found the skeleton of a young child – a victim of the times when women and children were employed in the mines.

In 1948, a miner working in the Lower Fenton seam at Rockingham Colliery

ABOVE: Stacks of timber props were a common sight in the stockyards of collieries in the days before mechanised roof supports were introduced. This large load was photographed at Ayrshire's Auchincruive Colliery (also known as Glenburn) as ex-LMS 2-6-0 No. 42739 arrived on a brakevan tour in April 1965. COLOUR-RAIL

found a newspaper dated 1912. Looking up, he noticed that it had fallen through a small hole from the abandoned Upper Fenton seam, which was sealed off, not having been used for years.

In the very early days, the more unscrupulous miners or coal owners had not been above taking coal from seams belonging to a neighbouring pit and claiming ignorance if caught out, but that practice was stamped out in the late Victorian era when it was decreed that all underground mine plans had to be deposited with the Mines Inspectorate.

It also became necessary to make test boreholes well in advance of the coal or rock that was about to be cut, to ensure that unrecorded old workings or large deposits of gas or water were not lying in wait. This was particularly important in coastal locations, where workings often extended miles under the sea. Collieries with such roadways included Ellington, in County Durham, Point of Ayr in North Wales and Haig in Cumbria. ●

ABOVE: The modern way of building roadways was to do so with roof bolts rather than with props or metal arches. Long bolts and quick-setting resin were inserted into self-supporting rock by special machines such as this and protective netting fitted to prevent small falls of rock from the surface.

THE **MACHINE** AGE

ABOVE: A longwall coalface in a modern British mine, showing the shearer/loader in action, the armoured face conveyor and the self-advancing powered roof supports. Note how far the longwall extends into the distance (some could be several hundred metres in length) and the fact that the operator is wearing face mask, ear defenders, eye protectors and shinguards as well as the traditional helmet. UK COAL

ABOVE: 'Distance no object', proclaims the advertisement in this 1960s colliery managers' yearbook. This particular model was a world-beater at the time, using just one drive unit to send coal four miles from face to shaft bottom.

ONE of the greatest priorities for the National Coal Board upon its formation in 1947 was the modernisation of the collieries – and that meant mechanisation.

A number of wealthier and more progressive coal-owning companies had been investing since the end of the 19th century in labour-saving devices such as compressed air-driven drills and saws, but even in the peak production year of 1913, only 8% of output was machine-cut.

Compressed air equipment was essential in 'gassy' mines where it was unsafe to use steam or electrical machinery underground. Some companies piped steam from surface-based boilers down the shaft, but condensation and pressure-drop at the point of use affected power output. Compressed air machinery was far more efficient but even that required enormous steam compressors on the surface with air pipes of up to a foot in diameter in the shaft.

During the 1920s and '30s, machine-cut output rose to more than 30% and most major collieries benefited from some form of coalface machinery, but many owners then put improvements on hold due to the Great Depression, the Second World War and the knowledge that nationalisation was pretty much inevitable. Only a programme of modernisation and mechanisation could save the industry.

Soon after winning the 1945 election, the Labour Government set up a body under Sir Charles Reid of the Fife Coal

Co to visit the United States and report on the mechanisation of the mines there. In addition to recommending the adoption of coal-cutting and loading machinery, the Reid Report advocated the widespread use of locomotive-operated railways on the basis that there's no point in mining coal faster than it can be taken to the shaft.

Over the next decade or so, expensive new hardware was purchased and installed at many of the NCB's 'premier league' mines:
• More longwall coalfaces were set up to make the most of the new cutter/loaders.
• Shafts were enlarged and equipped with faster, more powerful winding gear.
• Some coal-raising shafts were deepened and converted to skip-winding rather than cages and tubs. In other cases, surface drifts were driven for the installation of conveyors.
• Flame-proofed electrical machinery was introduced to replace compressed air equipment.
• Horse-drawn and rope-hauled underground transport was gradually replaced by trunk conveyors, gate conveyors and locomotive-powered rail systems.
• In mines that were not equipped with conveyors, half-ton tubs were replaced by two-ton or four-ton mine cars.

The trunk conveyors were also used later for the speedy movement of men to and from the coalface in districts where there was no rail transport available.

When it came to the use and manufacture of mechanised coal-cutting equipment, the USA was a world leader thanks in part to the pioneering efforts of inventors like David Joy, whose name is still well known in the mining world today. The Americans, however, stuck to pillar & stall working exclusively until the 1960s when the British were able to convince them that longwall was a superior system.

One of the earliest forms of equipment was a coal plough, which in its rudimentary form was literally dragged along the face by a chain and guiderail, slicing off coal as it went, but it required reasonably soft coal so could not be used in some locations.

In the early days of mechanisation, cutting machines were hauled along the face by a steel rope or, later, a chain anchored at the end, but after a number of serious accidents caused by chains breaking and ropes 'whipping' along the face, chainless methods such as rack & pinion began to be introduced.

A broken rope would thrash about for several seconds until its energy was dissipated, whereas a chain would kick just once when snapped and then lie still. Although a flying broken link could still kill anyone standing nearby, chains were considered much safer.

From early cutters were developed the various forms of cutter-loader, which delivered the freshly cut coal straight on to an armoured coalface conveyor to eliminate the need to gather it up by hand.

There were two basic forms of cutter - a trepanner (rather gruesomely so called because of its similarity to the surgical instrument used to drill small cylindrical holes in skulls) and a shearer, which worked more like a bacon slicer. The development of shearers that could cut in either direction, instead of having to return to the start each time, was a major breakthrough.

Mining techniques such as these also eliminated the need for drilling and blasting of the coalface and, in some cases, a machine was able to cut and load more coal in a few minutes than miners with picks and shovels could win in a whole day, although at first, allowances had to be made for the time it took to prepare each end of the face for the next cut. Until the advent of self-advancing roof supports, it was also a labour-intensive operation to manually move the hydraulic props and conveyor forward each time.

In 1947, 187million tons of coal had been produced by 707,000 miners (264 tons a man) and by 1973, 130m tons were produced by 268,000 miners (485 tons per man). That shows the effect of mechanisation.

Such automation greatly reduced the numbers of men at the coalface. What would have taken 50 men in 1947 was being done by perhaps five men by the end of the century, but at least remote control and monitoring were making it possible to remove humans from areas of potential danger.

This was particularly important given the unfortunate propensity of the early cutter/loaders to exacerbate two of the ever-present hazards facing coalminers; one was the amount of dust they threw up. Even with water jets on, it was so bad that men had to retreat to

On shift with the **'Widow-Maker'**

MOST early machinery was driven by compressed air for safety reasons, but some South Wales drift mines were classified as 'naked light' as they had no gas problems and could thus experiment with early electric machines. A 1920s description of one of the first American-built electric coal-cutters to work in Britain tells us that it was powered by a long thick high-voltage cable and drawn along by a steel rope travelling at about a yard a minute.

It was too wide for pit props to be placed as close to the face as in former days (powered props had not then been introduced) and if it did accidentally touch one of the timber posts, it would chew it to matchwood in seconds and could bring tons of rock crashing down.

That would not damage the machine as it was heavily armoured with thick steel plate, but it was extremely hazardous for the miners, who were unable to escape quickly if rocks did start falling. At least one man lost his life in a rock fall and the machine quickly became known as 'the widow-maker' – partly for that reason and partly because of the huge clouds of dust it threw up in the days before facemasks became readily available.

The falling stones also sometimes damaged the high-voltage cable, leaving the risk of a serious electric shock for anyone who accidentally came into contact with it.

Oblivious to the effect on the men who operated it, the mine company loved the machine's greatly increased productivity and soon extended the cutting targets from 150 yards a day to 500 yards (it had been a mere 12 yards when cut manually).

Imagine visiting the coalface when such a cutter was in operation. The machine would be roaring, the conveyor belt clanging and rattling, as many as 30 men would be shovelling coal into tubs, which would be rumbling along the rails behind horses. It was bedlam and many old miners from the much quieter manual days left the industry or sought work on the surface.

They had been brought up in a time when miners had a professional respect for the coal and worked it in a skilled and neat fashion – not by 'roughly dragging it out by the scruff of its neck'.

fresher air now and again, yet some of them still chose not to wear breathing masks or goggles.

The second was the noise. They kicked up such a racket in the confined space that they nullified one of the miners' most valuable senses. No longer could they hear the roof 'talking' to them - the tell-tale sound of a wooden pit prop starting to split, the ominous dribble of a little bit of dirt from a roof, a low groan somewhere from the bowels of the earth. All would warn the miner to run to a place of safety.

Not for nothing did those early machines begin to attract nicknames such as 'the widow maker' (see above).

Overall, the advantages of mechanisation outweighed the disadvantages, though… and some of the benefits hadn't been immediately obvious. Take Blaydon Burn Colliery, for instance, which in the 1950s had a seam of fine coking coal just 1ft 2in thick. This was virtually inaccessible until it was found that a remote-controlled scraper shearer machine could scrape 100 tons a day off the seam on to a conveyor belt running at right angles to it.

Away from the face, processes were being speeded up too. The 'Lambton Worm' in the Great Northern Coalfield worked on the principle of a roller-coaster, with a heavily twisting track causing a fast-running train of mine ▶

ABOVE: Adjustments being made to the top section of a trepanner-type coal cutter.

ABOVE: A mechanical undercutter machine. Undercutting, or kirving, of coal prior to shot-firing was a regular occurrence in mines until the advent of longwall shearers and was performed manually for many years.

cars to turn upside down so that the coal fell out of each one into a bunker or conveyor before they were returned the right way up again.

The conveyors themselves became wider, faster, stronger and steeper and, on the surface, automation in the coal preparation plants (CPPs) meant that they could be left to operate all day with only minimal supervision. The development of new roadways and faces was also sped up by the use of caterpillar-tracked road-header machines loading on to conveyors and doing away with much of the time-consuming blasting and hand-hewing methods of old.

By the 1960s, the world was entering an era of increasing energy alternatives with the growing popularity of gas, oil and nuclear power, and the NCB and its political masters decided that the only way to restore coal's competitiveness was to reduce costs by further mechanising selected large collieries and closing small or high-cost pits not considered worth modernising. This involved enormous capital investment by the Government of the day, for even in the 1960s and '70s, the development cost of a single face could run into several million pounds.

By that time, there were even nucleonic-steered shearers that could sense automatically the difference between roof stone and coal and thus reduce the amount of waste rock sent to the surface with the coal. These worked by using a cobalt power source to emit particles towards the roof and then measuring the back-scatter to gauge the thickness, as the amounts reflected by coal and stone are different. A small computer in the shearer adjusted the cutting head accordingly. After years of experience, this system was adjudged to be more trouble than it was worth.

As such devices were not common anyway, mechanisation of thin or disturbed seams meant that as much as 30% dirt was being loaded with the coal at some Lancashire collieries following

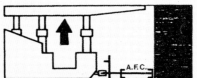

STEP A
The vertical supports are extended to bring the roof beam into contact with the newly exposed roof.

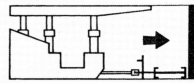

STEP B
The power-loader has passed on the loading run and the double-acting ram is extended, pushing forward the conveyor.

STEP C
The vertical supports are lowered.

STEP D
The ram is set into reverse and the support is drawn up to the new face line. It is then reset to the roof (step A).

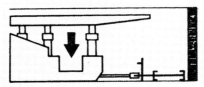

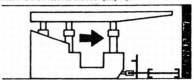

ABOVE: The four stages by which a hydraulic roof-support advanced itself towards the coalface in relation to the armoured face conveyor (AFC) and the power-loader coal-cutting machine.

mechanisation, hence the need for CPPs. See page 80.

The modernisation programme nevertheless enabled massive improvements to be made. As an example, an investment of half a million pounds in South Yorkshire's Wentworth Silkstone Colliery in the early 1950s saw it gain a CPP and a trunk conveyor system linking the face with the plant. This resulted in a huge increase in efficiency almost overnight and its annual output more than doubled from 160,000 tons to 345,000.

Even more successful was the modernised Linby mine, in Nottinghamshire, recognised as the most efficient in the whole of Europe at one time. It had a workforce of only 1,100 but was one of only three collieries in the UK producing more than a million tons a year in those formative NCB days.

Perhaps the most significant development of the modernisation programme, however, was the way the roof was supported at the coalface. Traditionally, timber props had been placed under the roof and tightened with wooden lids knocked into place with sledgehammers; then came hydraulically operated metal

props and finally self-advancing powered supports.

The hydraulic mechanism on the latter could be operated so that they would move themselves towards the face after the shearer had passed, and also so that their roof-supporting components could be elevated to take the strain of the rock above. One machine on its own would not have been able to bear such a weight, but by lining up dozens and dozens of powered roof supports alongside each other, an entire section of newly exposed roof could be supported above the length of a longwall face.

Powered supports meant a prop-free front and as that was considered extremely risky at the time, the approval of the Mines Inspectorate was required before such equipment could even be tried. However, the cutting machines moved along the face fairly quickly and could be controlled remotely from a position of safety on the goaf side of the conveyor, so the roof was unsupported for only the few minutes it took a miner to operate the hydraulic mechanism. In that time, the weight of the roof would be taken by the supports either side of the one being moved.

The only other thing the operators had to do once the cutter had passed was to move the armoured flexible conveyor by hydraulic ram towards the newly exposed part of the face. (The conveyor was composed of loosely linked sections so that it could be 'snaked' into position). The powered supports could then be quickly moved in behind it, also by hydraulic force. That way, men did not have to enter the unsupported section.

The fact that both the cutters and the conveyors were heavily armoured meant that they would not be damaged if any part of the roof did happen to fall. Developed by the German mining industry, armoured face conveyors were appropriately known (by the NCB as well as the men) as 'Panzers'.

Automation of the coal-cutting process was known as continuous mining and was so successful that coal

ABOVE: Powered roof supports weren't only built for seams of 4ft thickness and more. These miniature versions were supplied for very thin seams in South Wales and were photographed at **Lewis Merthyr Colliery.** NICK PIGOTT

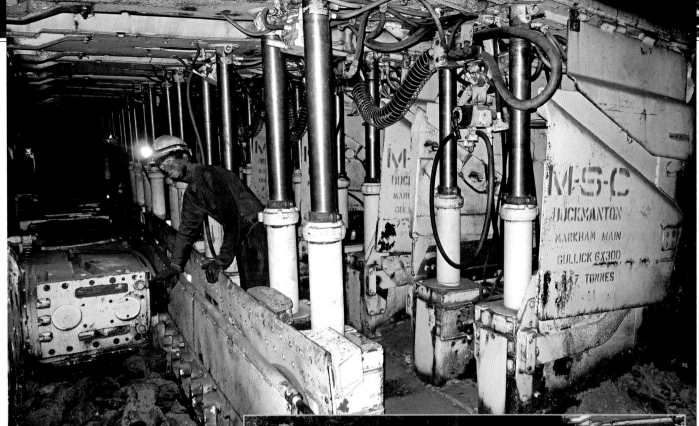

ABOVE AND RIGHT: Roof supports and cutter head on display in the coalface section of the Scottish Mining Museum at Lady Victoria Colliery.

RECORD BREAKER

AS if to show his new masters at the NCB what an individual miner could do with only minimal mechanised aids, 37-year-old South Wales miner Edwin Slade of Pontycynmer created a world record in 1947 when he won 120 tons of coal during a six-week shift at International Colliery, Blaengarw, using a hand-held pneumatically powered pick working a 4ft seam. To achieve that, he also had to shift 20 tons of 'clod' (waste).

became competitive on the world markets again.

By the mid-1970s, more than 90% of all coal was being won by cutter/loaders. Three-quarters of Britain's coalfaces used shearers, 22% used trepanners and the remaining 3% mainly used ploughs. Hand-winning of coal had thus been totally eradicated everywhere except in a tiny handful of small privately owned drift mines.

Following the installation of such machinery in large NCB pits, output of a million tons a year per colliery became reasonably frequent. The British mine that hit the magic million tons in the shortest time was Bentinck, Nottinghamshire, which in 1969 achieved it by July 25, not much more than halfway through the year.

Automation allowed coal preparation plants to be left to run virtually all day without human involvement and huge reductions became possible in the size of teams at the coalface, where a single powered

ABOVE: So many miles from shaft bottom were some coalfaces that special dispensation was given for miners to ride on conveyor belts if the rail tracks did not extend far enough. Note the miner at the higher level travelling in the opposite direction.

roof support could have as many as three micro-computers managing its automated functions.

Even the underground environment could be checked from a surface-based control room, enabling critical factors such as gas concentrations, ventilation and temperature readings to be monitored remotely and adjusted if necessary. ●

LIFE ON THE TOP

A BIG colliery in the heyday of mining was effectively a self-contained industrial plant, employing its own fitters, mechanics, electricians, welders, joiners, blacksmiths, bricklayers, plumbers, farriers, stable lads, engine crews, shunters, cage-smiths and wagon repairers, not to mention office-based staff, such as managers, surveyors, accountants and clerks.

The nationalised era saw much of the routine overhaul of machinery transferred to central workshops, which served several mines – but the pits themselves retained a surprisingly high number of surface-based disciplines, particularly electricians, fitters, loco drivers and office staff.

In the years before the National Grid, many of the larger collieries had to generate all their own power, which they mainly did via large stationary steam engines, but from the late Victorian period onwards, several possessed their own small power stations and electricity networks. They were able to do away with those once the Grid had been fully established in 1938, but the last few self-contained NCB electricity networks weren't discontinued until the 1970s.

Up until that point, quite a few collieries had supplied their local village with power, but to prevent abuse or wastage of this facility, some had a system whereby if a householder attempted to have more than three 60-watt bulbs on at the same time, a switch would kick in and flick the lights on and off until the load was reduced!

Photographs of collieries in the early half of the century often show plumes of steam emanating from various places. In addition to the winding engines, there were steam-driven compressors for machinery underground and steam-driven turbines for machinery on the surface. Many ventilation fans were also steam-powered and in winter months, large braziers would be used at the top of the downcast shaft to warm the air before it entered the mine to prevent the pipes in the shaft from freezing.

ABOVE: Among the many items of machinery found on the surface of a traditional colliery were stationary boilers. These were used for heating or powering of plant and were of several types – 'Egg-ended' and Lancashire types being the most common. Four of the latter are seen at Staffordshire's Chatterley Whitfield Colliery in September 2015. NICK PIGOTT

BELOW: The stock yards of major collieries were almost businesses in their own right, holding and supplying replacement parts for the thousands of different components used above and below the ground. This was part of the sprawling yard at Markham Colliery in March 1993. NICK PIGOTT

Lorries
Do not park
on the road.

MARKHAM COLLIERY
Landsale
Coal Prep. Plant
Coal Bagging Plant
Wagon Tipping
Stockyard

YOU ARE ENTERING
A SAFETY ZONE
HAVE A SAFE DAY

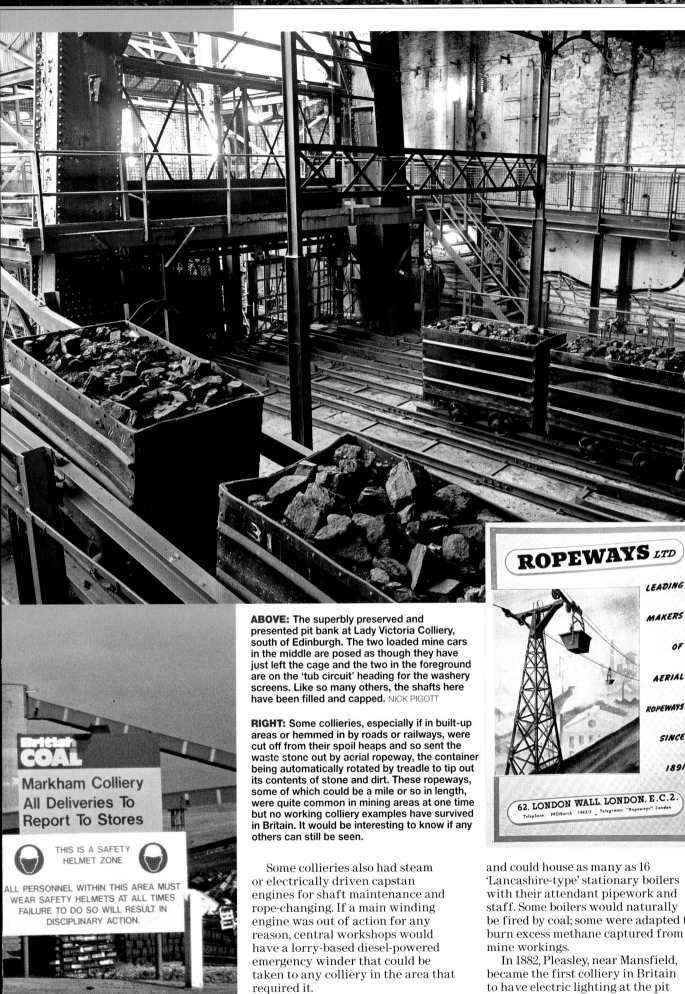

ABOVE: The superbly preserved and presented pit bank at Lady Victoria Colliery, south of Edinburgh. The two loaded mine cars in the middle are posed as though they have just left the cage and the two in the foreground are on the 'tub circuit' heading for the washery screens. Like so many others, the shafts here have been filled and capped. NICK PIGOTT

RIGHT: Some collieries, especially if in built-up areas or hemmed in by roads or railways, were cut off from their spoil heaps and so sent the waste stone out by aerial ropeway, the container being automatically rotated by treadle to tip out its contents of stone and dirt. These ropeways, some of which could be a mile or so in length, were quite common in mining areas at one time but no working colliery examples have survived in Britain. It would be interesting to know if any others can still be seen.

Some collieries also had steam or electrically driven capstan engines for shaft maintenance and rope-changing. If a main winding engine was out of action for any reason, central workshops would have a lorry-based diesel-powered emergency winder that could be taken to any colliery in the area that required it.

All those steam-powered machines were fed by the boiler house, some of which were absolutely immense

and could house as many as 16 'Lancashire-type' stationary boilers with their attendant pipework and staff. Some boilers would naturally be fired by coal; some were adapted to burn excess methane captured from the mine workings.

In 1882, Pleasley, near Mansfield, became the first colliery in Britain to have electric lighting at the pit bottom and 1910 saw the country's first all-electric mine – Britannia, Monmouthshire.

ABOVE: Following the introduction of 'Merry-go-Round' (MGR) deliveries of pulverised coal direct from colliery to power station, huge rapid loaders were constructed. BR Coal sector-allocated Class 58 No. 58004 takes a train through the loader at Bentinck Colliery on January 22, 1994. RAIL PHOTOPRINTS

Electric generators and dynamos didn't simply allow use of electric tools and winding gear, they generated power to operate compressed-air equipment too.

The amount of separate surface buildings to be found on a typical coalmine site was impressive: not immediately springing to mind for most people asked to make a list of such buildings would be the powder magazine (explosives store). These were always located well away from the other surface structures and kept securely locked when not in use. When underground, explosives and detonators were almost invariably kept apart from each other and were carried in specially modified drams or wagons.

In areas where the coal was suitable, many large mines also had a coking works attached to them (see page 96). Others, especially in the Midlands, were accompanied by a brickworks. Bricks became cheaper to make when coal, rather than charcoal, was used to bake them and in some cases, the clay was produced from the mine. In others, an opencast clay hole might be dug.

ABOVE: Lagoons and settling ponds were common sights at collieries in their heyday, but although Pleasley Colliery has escaped demolition, this view from April 1984 is no longer possible as the reservoir has been filled in. ROBIN STEWART-SMITH

ABOVE: Despite the introduction of a network of central workshops as part of an early NCB initiative, some collieries retained their individual workshop buildings, some of which were huge, such as this one at Thoresby.

ABOVE: The upcast winder cable drum at Pleasley Colliery, seen during an open day in September 2015. Both the steam winding engines at this mine near Mansfield have been preserved and it is eventually hoped to have both working.

ABOVE: Possibly the last photograph ever taken of a rail vehicle loaded with underground supplies being pushed into the cage of a British deep colliery. It was taken on the pit bank at Kellingley shortly before the mine's closure. NICK PIGOTT

The NCB inherited 85 brickworks in 1947, producing about 400million bricks a year. The NCB itself consumed about 25% of the bricks made by its collieries, using them for construction of new mine buildings and for lining shafts and pit bottom areas. By 1973, only 19 brickworks remained and they were sold that year to the private sector, but a reminder of the old days can be found in 2016 by the presence of a brickyard on the site of Desford Colliery, Leics.

Because the sheer volume of large heavy equipment required down a mine was so great – especially while new roads were being driven and new faces opened up – it was normally necessary to have a large open-air compound on the colliery premises in which to store roof-supporting arches, spare items of machinery, lengths of railway track and, in former years, freshly delivered timber props and so on. These large areas were additional to the colliery stores building, where small items were kept.

One of the largest buildings at a traditional major colliery would have been the workshop for repairing, maintaining and even manufacturing equipment. Railway locomotives were sometimes overhauled in them too.

A tall factory-style chimney was a common sight at a traditional mine. They were normally there to create a draught for the boilers. The steam winding engines exhausted separately (or their steam was condensed and the water reused), while the ventilation fan exhausted through a short concrete or metal tower called an evasee. It was important to keep the gassy air and coal dust extracted by the fan separate from any other form of chimney due to the risk of an explosion.

Grimethorpe (few names summed up the Southerners' perception of a colliery location better than that!) was one of many gassy mines with a methane-drainage system, which recovered burnable gas for the boilers. Piping the gas to the surface also reduced its concentration.

Methane-exhausting pipes can still be seen on the sites of several demolished collieries to this day, even in the midst of some modern housing estates – and there are two black pipes near the car park of Sunderland FC's Stadium of Light, which are there to let methane escape from the old Wearmouth Colliery workings.

In addition to the headgear, some modern mines possessed other tall concrete structures, similar to silos. These were pit top bunkers that could be used either for blending coal of different qualities or for regularising the coal flow to the preparation plant so that, if a delay occurred, the storage facilities could be used and the winding of coal would not be affected. This was the practice at Kellingley right to the end, although there the coal was deposited on to a pile in the open air rather than in a bunker. At its peak in the 1960s, Calverton Colliery was operating nine faces at once, hence the need for storage and blending bunkers.

Other large buildings were coal preparation plants, rapid-loading bunkers for transferring coal to railway wagons, and water/slurry towers. ▶

Smaller surface structures included drift top terminals, fan houses, timber stockyards, engine sheds, lamp rooms, pump houses, stores, blacksmiths' forges, joiners' shops, electricians' and fitters' cabins, administrative offices, medical centres, shower and canteen blocks and, in later years, a spider's web of covered conveyers linking numerous parts of the colliery network.

In recent years, remote control and computerisation equipment was installed on the surface to automatically operate underground conveyors, bunkers, pumps and fans. At some collieries whose coal-raising shafts were equipped for skip-loading, even the headgear

Pithead Baths: **Doing away with the Tin Bathtub**

IN 1951, a National Coal Board official stated: "It is our aim that every miner in every pit should be able to go home clean!" and from then onwards, a massive programme of pithead bath installations was implemented.

Surprisingly, not every collier welcomed these improvements at first. Some were naturally embarrassed at having to strip naked and shower in front of their workmates, but the main reason for resistance was a long-standing superstition among the older men that washing one's back and leg muscles every day permanently weakened them.

Hard though it might be to believe now, such men believed that it was better simply to ask their wife to 'polish' their coaldust-covered back and only wash it properly once a week, or even once a month. Old-time colliers who had started work in the 19th century also had a superstition that washing their backs would cause a roof fall. No doubt plenty of pyjamas had to be used in such households to keep the bed linen clean!

Pithead baths (more usually showers) had been in use in France, Belgium and Germany since the 1880s and one or two English collieries had such facilities – Gibfield in Lancashire, for instance. In 1913, just before the First World War broke out, the Ocean Coal Company of Wales sent a delegation to Europe to study the baths there and report back. This led to the opening of an architecturally imposing bath house at Deep Navigation Colliery, Teharris, in 1916.

Other British coal companies were not so progressive and although a Pithead Baths Movement had been formed in the 1890s to campaign for such facilities, it was 1919 before the British Government set up a commission to investigate living conditions in the coalfields. As a result, a miners' welfare fund was established to build libraries, institutes, playing fields, canteens and other facilities for mining communities, funded by a levy of a penny on every ton of coal mined. In 1926, an additional levy was raised specifically for colliery-based showers and nearly 400 collieries benefited between then and the advent of the National Coal Board 21 years later.

Before the improvements, miners had had no choice but to walk home dirty and wash in a tin bath at home, for which their womenfolk would have to have boiled several pans and kettles beforehand on an open coal fire. The physical strain associated with the daily lifting of the heavy baths, pans, tubs and boilers necessary for such work is reported to have contributed to the majority of miscarriages and other female ailments in the coalfields.

ABOVE: Very few miners' cottages had bathrooms, so before the installation of pithead showers, colliers had to walk home dirty and use a tin bath in front of the living room fire. The rest of the family treated this as normal, even diligently concentrating on their school homework in the case of these two daughters.

In homes in which there were several working miners, a strict seniority pecking order would be in effect with the father or grandfather getting the clean water and the youngest son having to sit in the dirty lukewarm slop vacated by perhaps three or four others.

The showers themselves weren't the only improvements brought about by the bath construction programme, for they were accompanied by changing rooms in which two lockers were provided for every member of staff – one for dirty, wet clothes and the other (on the other side of the shower block) for clean, dry attire. Warm air from the boilerhouse was also blown through the dirty lockers to ensure overalls were dry the next day.

CANTEENS: Progressive coal owners from the 1920s and '30s onwards, and the NCB after 1947, ensured that pithead canteens were provided at most large and medium-sized collieries. In addition to hot meals, these sold snacks, soft drinks, soap, towels and other essentials. They also sold snuff and chewing tobacco (known as a 'twist')… but not pipe tobacco or cigarettes, which were classed as contraband (see Safety section on page 95).

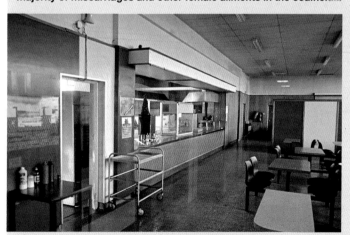

ABOVE: Food for thought: The very last of all the pit canteens in a British working colliery, still serving meals when this picture was taken at Kellingley in November 2015. The poster on the left wall invited miners and their families to a pit party on Saturday, December 19… the day after the mine's closure.

ABOVE: The pithead baths at Kellingley Colliery were some of the largest in the country, enabling almost 100 miners to shower simultaneously. NICK PIGOTT

was automatically controlled.

Add the omnipresent spoil tip, more often than not towering over the scene like a brooding mountain, and some larger collieries could extend for well over a mile in length. ●

Warning
In case of nuclear attack please hide under litter bins, nothing ever hits them

ABOVE: Mineworkers were renowned for their sense of humour, as evidenced by this sign at Rufford Colliery in 1992. NICK PIGOTT

ABOVE: An aspect of surface working now long disappeared was the rope haulage system. This enabled standard gauge wagons to be raised and lowered on far steeper inclines than would be possible with locomotive haulage. This example was photographed at Kilmersdon Colliery in the Somerset coalfield in February 1970. COLOUR-RAIL

By Royal **Appointment**

ABOVE: Admiring glances from miners as Her Majesty the Queen pays a visit to Silverwood Colliery on July 31, 1975, one of several underground trips the monarch has made in her 64 years on the throne. (It is not known how often she managed to keep those white overalls clean!)

COAL mines have had their fair share of royal visits over the years. Kings George V and George VI helped keep the nation's morale up with visits during the war years to places such as Elsecar and Hickleton Main in 1944, and the current Elizabethan era has also seen a number of high-profile VIP tours.

Two involved unexpected consequences. When Princess Margaret made her first visit down a mine during the official opening of Calverton Colliery on September 24, 1952, she was shown two of the mine's three faces. When the men working the third face asked afterwards why she had not visited them, they were told that it was "too perilous"... so they promptly demanded danger money!

The other occasion occurred at Bevercotes Colliery on the night before the Duke of Edinburgh was due to make a formal visit. Although his visit had been pre-arranged, it coincided with an unexpected lull in production – so an anxious Bevercotes manager arranged for a load of freshly dug coal to be brought over from Ollerton Colliery, a few miles away in the same Nottinghamshire coalfield. He then arranged for it to be deposited at the coal face and, after the royal visit was over, had it returned whence it came. It is said that the Duke never suspected!

When he visited Silverwood Colliery in 1975, it was in the company of the Queen, who was neatly attired in pure white overalls, as she had been at Rothes Colliery in 1954.

On the subject of cleanliness, Newstead Colliery was one of those that had the honour at one time of supplying coal to Buckingham Palace – but it had to be hand-picked... and whitewashed!

Numerous VIPs and politicians were also afforded the privilege of an underground visit, the most controversial being that of Prime Minister Thatcher to Yorkshire's Wistow Colliery in February 1980 – four years before the devastating miners' strike began.

ABOVE: Tending to his flock thousands of feet below the soil... the Archbishop of Canterbury, the Rt Rev Donald Coggan, during a visit to the Kentish coalfield in the 1970s. J DAVIES

ABOVE: If a competition was held to decide which English county was the most unlikely to have a coal-mining connection, Surrey would be close to the top of most people's lists – so this kneeling mat inside Guildford Cathedral is something of an incongruity!

MAKING THE COAL
FIT TO SELL

ABOVE: In the days before coal preparation plants, the waste stone was picked from the coal by hand by pit brow lasses, 10 of whom are working with three men in this early 20th century view of a picking belt.

THE coal that came up to the surface was referred to as 'Run of Mine' and was usually mixed with shale and other forms of non-flammable rock from the strata above and below the coal seam.

In order to make it marketable, it had to be cleaned and graded and this is where screens and washeries came into play.

Almost every colliery in the 20th century had some form of screen building - or at least the use of one within a short distance - and from the middle of the century onwards, the major modernised mines began to have their washeries replaced by larger, more sophisticated installations known as coal preparation plants (CPPs).

A CPP improves marketability by removing stone and dirt and by sizing and grading the product to ensure that a higher proportion is saleable. It also improves profitability by reclaiming small pieces of coal that would otherwise have ended up on the waste tip.

The old form of screens basically comprised a large elevated building on strong steel, concrete or timber stilts straddling a row of sidings on which would stand main line railway wagons. Most buildings contained rudimentary washing facilities and some form of conveyor known as a 'picking belt', beside which would stand workers who hand-sorted the coal and identified the shale and other rocks - quickly lifting them off the belt and throwing them on to a waste pile.

Such visual separation of unwanted minerals was to continue at some collieries for many years, but the sizing part of the process soon began to be semi-automated by the introduction of sieves. With these, the approved coal would enter a mesh section of the mechanism, which automatically separated it, the smallest pieces falling through the first set of sieves and the

BELOW: In recent years, coal preparation plants became smaller as pumps took over from gravity feed for movement of the fluids through the system. This one at Thoresby Colliery in 2015 had been at Daw Mill until two years earlier, being moved in component form and re-erected at its new location. NICK PIGOTT

ABOVE: A rarely seen view taken from the top level of a full-size gravity-fed coal preparation plant, in operation showing the water rushing through the washbox far below. A description of the coal washing and reclamation process can be found in the main text. NICK PIGOTT

largest continuing along a belt until reaching the furthest and widest apertures. In each case, they would fall by gravity into the waiting railway wagons below – a minimum of one row of wagons for each size.

Anything that didn't go into the main line wagons was sent to the spoil tip, usually by conveyor belt or aerial ropeway. At some pits, the screens would have a siding for a line of internal wagons to catch the dirt, which would then be hauled away to the tip by one of the colliery's own locomotives.

Depending on how efficient the exterior cladding was, a thick pall of dust could often be seen hanging around the outside of a washery building whenever the screens were in operation, obscuring the structure and making driving conditions hazardous if there were any roads nearby.

Removing waste from run-of-mine (ROM) coal was important as it reduced impurities and thus increased the value of the product by making it more attractive to customers. By taking out heavy stone, it also reduced transport costs.

Many of the picking table workers were females, displaced from their duties underground as a result of law ▶

ABOVE: The screens at Mansfield Colliery, seen here in 1989, were a good example of the long multi-tracked type found at many large collieries in earlier decades.
ROBIN STEWART-SMITH

ABOVE: Beamish Colliery is now believed to be the only place in England where traditional colliery screens can be seen. Lewin 0-4-0ST No. 18 is pictured underneath them with a rake of chaldron waggons in April 2016. NICK PIGOTT

How a typical **Coal Preparation Plant** works

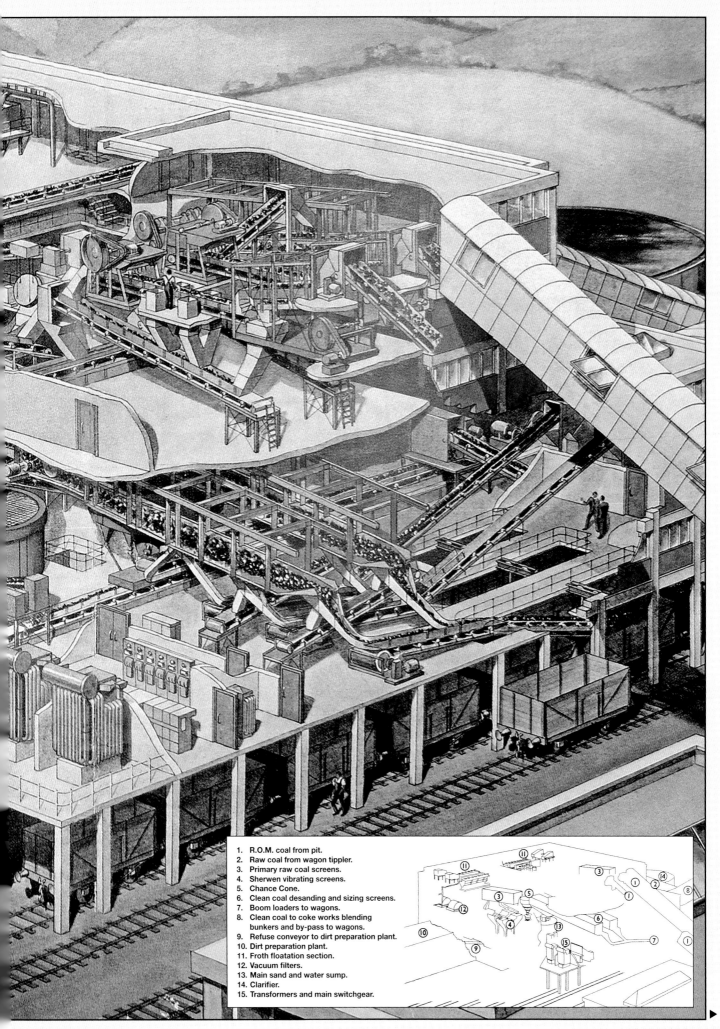

1. R.O.M. coal from pit.
2. Raw coal from wagon tippler.
3. Primary raw coal screens.
4. Sherwen vibrating screens.
5. Chance Cone.
6. Clean coal desanding and sizing screens.
7. Boom loaders to wagons.
8. Clean coal to coke works blending bunkers and by-pass to wagons.
9. Refuse conveyor to dirt preparation plant.
10. Dirt preparation plant.
11. Froth floatation section.
12. Vacuum filters.
13. Main sand and water sump.
14. Clarifier.
15. Transformers and main switchgear.

DID YOU **KNOW?**

Coal is sold in many different sizes, the main ones being: Large, Cobbles, Doubles, Singles, Cubes, Nuts, Middlings, Smalls, Beans, Peas, Grains, Slack and Culm.

ABOVE: A general view of Kellingley Colliery. The large building in the middle was the coal preparation plant.

changes in the Victorian era (see page 34), and they would be supplemented by young lads of about 14-16, and former miners, some of whom had perhaps suffered serious injury in the past and were no longer up to working at the coalface. It was boring, repetitive and demanding work that required constant attention, but it provided regular employment.

A coal preparation plant, on the other hand, was a totally different beast altogether and the National Coal Board built about 200 of these huge modern structures between

1947 and 1956, following that up with the modernisation of less sophisticated ones it had inherited at 170 or so other collieries.

In a CPP, automated machinery and complicated technology took the place of humans, sorting or crushing the coal to the required sizes, reducing the waste and sulphur content and making the mine far more efficient and profitable. Not only did it take the laborious manpower out of coal separation and sizing but it retrieved tiny particles of dust and broken coal, which had previously been

allowed to go to waste as the majority of customers in the early years wanted only larger lumps of coal for domestic or industrial use.

In fact, some coal mine owners in the Victorian era had refused to pay their self-employed or piece-rate colliers anything for small coal even though it had been hewed from the coalface! The advent of large coal-fired power stations in the second half of the 20th century changed all that, as most required pulverised coal.

Although all Britain's deep mines have now closed, a few preparation units remain in operation at surface mines, where the more productive but less selective nature of opencast excavation makes it harder to produce coal clean enough for sale without processing.

Designs of CPP differed depending on the manufacturer, but a great many British collieries were equipped with the Baum system, based on a design

ABOVE AND RIGHT: A peep into the top of a high-level Baum tower containing unclarified liquid and (right) one containing water after clarification.

by German engineer Fritz Baum. Its principle of operation hinges on the fact that coal has a lower density than shale and other rock and will thus 'float' if placed in a denser liquid.

After passing under a powerful electro-magnet (to remove bits of wire and scrap metal that may have been picked up underground), the minerals enter a large 'washbox' whose water has been made denser by the addition of sand or a pulverised iron oxide such as magnetite. Bursts of compressed air are sent through the liquid and cause the mixed coal, shale and dirt to become separated into different layers as they are jigged about. The heaviest pieces of stone sink immediately and are removed from the plant.

The coal and middle-sized pieces of waste then pass into a secondary compartment, from where the dirt drops through a screen to be discarded while the clean coal flows out over the top of the tank and is taken for classifying.

The process is linked with another environmentally friendly procedure - the recycling of water. As the dirty fluid leaves the washbox, it is pumped to the top of a Baum tower, a conical concrete settling and clarifying tank. There, the solids are allowed to slowly sink to the bottom and form a slurry while the clear water at the top is piped to the washbox for re-use, the height of the tower giving it the required pressure. The slurry is not allowed to go to waste and is drawn off from the bottom and sent to de-watering screens, which filter out the coarser coal particles - but some of the ultrafine ones remain suspended in the water.

They are thus moved to what is known as the 'froth flotation process'. This is an ingenious system in which a frothing agent is added to the water to create bubbles and the minute particles of coal are persuaded to stick to the outside of the bubbles by means of surface tension and 'hitch a ride' to the top. The equally tiny particles of dirt, being a fraction heavier, remain behind.

The coal-laden froth is skimmed off and moved to a bath beneath a large, hollow rotating metal drum, inside which a vacuum has been created. As the drum slowly rotates through the froth, the vacuum causes the particles to adhere to a belt around the drum, forming a filter cake, which is then blown off by air and collected.

The dirt and clay particles (known as 'tailings') left behind in the froth then have a chemical added to them to make them flocculate into slightly larger clumps and are sent to a clarifying tank known as a thickener, where they are churned by revolving rakes and sink to the bottom to leave clear and reusable water on top. The sediment is then sent to a de-watering press from where it is safely disposed

of while the liquid is pumped back for re-use. This effective closed-circuit ensures that no polluted effluent finds its way into natural water courses.

It might be wondered why so much effort is invested in retrieving particles of coal almost too small to be seen by the naked eye, but it has to be remembered that modern British collieries large enough to warrant a preparation plant were capable of producing at least a million tonnes of coal a year and that most of that was sent in crushed form to power station boilers. In earlier years, when most colliery output had to be in the form of large chunks of coal for household or railway use, it wouldn't have been economic to process the small stuff in the slurry, but a big 'prep plant' can recover between 100 and 200 tons of tiny particles a day and when all that microscopic material is added together over the course of a year,

it can amount to 70,000 tons of profitable coal.

The other reason, of course, is that without the CPPs, it was difficult to get water clean enough to recycle efficiently into the system, meaning that collieries would constantly have to be paying for fresh water supplies. Another advantage is that they help reduce harmful emissions by removing so many impurities.

Coal preparation plants have traditionally been large tall buildings with multiple levels to maximise the use of gravity flow, but towards the end of the deep mining industry there was a trend towards single-level facilities with more of the slurry being moved by pumps instead of gravity. A couple of years before its 2015 closure, an example of this more modern type was moved by UK Coal from Daw Mill to Thoresby to replace a life-expired multiple-level facility at the latter colliery. ●

The many uses for **Coal**

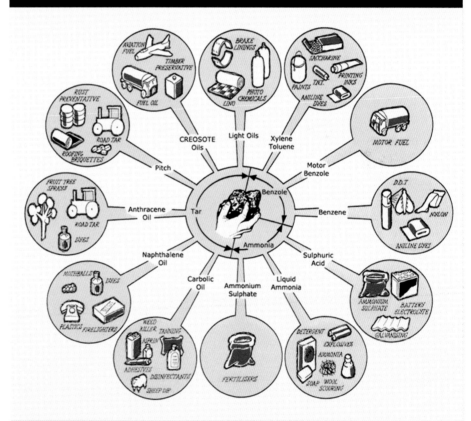

ABOVE: A diagram showing some of the many remarkably varied uses to which coal and its by-products can be used. COURTESY HEALEYHERO.CO.UK

A SURPRISING variety of everyday household products are created from coal and there are many other uses to which the by-products of coal and coke have been put to, once processed (some indirectly).

The main by-products are benzene, ammonia and tar, and from those, combined with other ingredients, can be gained the following:

Margarine, washing powder, baking powder, soap, mothballs, nylon, linoleum, aspirin, saccharin, waxed toilet paper, wax oil, fertilisers, sheep dips, weedkillers, insecticides, disinfectants, sulphuric acid, road tar, dyes, explosives, firelighters, adhesives, plastics, motor fuel, aviation fuel, creosote, brake linings, linoleum, photo chemicals, golf balls, clay pigeons, inks, paints ... and even perfume!

MAN-MADE
MOUNTAINS

IN the Wigan area of Lancashire in the 1930s, author George Orwell referred to a 'lunar landscape of slag heaps' as far as the eye could see and recorded that they were often on fire.

"At night, you can see the red rivulets of fire winding this way and that. Overhead were steel pylons and cables where tubs of dirt travel slowly across the countryside."

His vivid description could have described almost any coalfield scene, for the heaps towered over almost every colliery and told travellers for miles around that they were approaching a mining community.

Even today, it is still possible with a trained eye to detect the sites of many former collieries from their tips even though they've usually been landscaped or planted with grass or trees and turned into country parks.

The tendency of tips to smoulder or burst into flames spontaneously led during the Second World War to water having to be sprayed on to some of them to stop them giving the position of the mine away to enemy bombers.

Spoil heaps are sometimes known as shale heaps as that's what many of them largely comprise. Other terms are waste heaps, pit hills, muck stacks, batches or bings, the various terms emanating from different geographical regions with bing being more widely used in Scotland and muck stack in Yorkshire.

The term 'slag heap' is used extensively by the popular media, but is, strictly speaking, incorrect as slag is a product of the ore-smelting industry. Few working in the coal industry

BELOW: A highly nostalgic and evocative landscape portraying the coal mining industry in its NCB heyday. The year is 1966 and British Railways Class 4MT 2-6-0 No. 43123 is running past Ashington Colliery's spoil heap with a train of loaded BR coal wagons as the mine's aerial ropeway goes about its business. Note the protective structure erected over the railway to prevent spillages of rock and spoil falling on to trains or even on to the nearby signalbox. On the right, a crane is loading a rake of wooden-bodied internal user wagons. RAIL PHOTOPRINTS

would have used such a phrase except perhaps as a slang term. Waste was, however, also known as dirt, discard, reject, rubbish or rock.

The aerial ropeways that sometimes linked the heaps to the collieries also had a nickname, being called in some areas 'Blondins' after the French tightrope walker.

Some spoil heaps can cover several acres and be more than a mile long and members of the public could be forgiven for wondering why so much waste was produced by the mining industry: it didn't used to be. When coal was worked by hand in the 19th century, colliers were paid less if they allowed too much dirt to enter their tubs, so it was in their interests to ensure as little wastage as possible was sent to the surface.

The waste stone was often used to fill the goaf and to build packs along the roadways - but in the second half of the 20th century, the whole seam, including dirt bands and adjacent stone, was wrenched off by machines and transferred directly

ABOVE: Many large spoil heaps were graded level on the top by earth-moving equipment but some retained their characteristic cone shapes. This was Blaenafon Colliery tip, seen with Barclay 0-4-0ST *Nora* in March 1973. In later years, many tips grew much larger than this. BRIAN SHARPE

to conveyor belts, so perhaps only 70-80% of what was wound to the surface was coal.

In fact, at Kent's Betteshanger Colliery (which didn't close until 1989), as much as two tons of dirt was produced for every ton of clean coal and it was said that the waste tip there was the largest ongoing civil engineering site in the county apart from the Channel Tunnel construction site!

As explained earlier in the previous chapter, it was possible to compensate for this apparent flagrancy by enormous advances in coal washing and preparation techniques, with highly efficient automatic screens and reclamation systems doing what huge teams of pickers used to do.

Given the number of years such mechanised operations sent the waste to the tips - half a century or more in the case of the recently closed mines at Hatfield and Thoresby - it's easy to understand why heaps grew to such enormous sizes in the latter half of the 20th century. Hatfield's even hit national headlines in 2013 when part of it slid down and undermined all four tracks of a main railway, which had to be closed for several months while the spoil was removed and the line rebuilt.

In the early 1960s, environmental issues began to see a change of policy at some locations, with waste and dirt being stowed in the void left by the extracted coal instead of being taken to the surface. This had the benefit of reducing subsidence as well as the size of the spoil heaps.

Kellingley Colliery was one that ceased to use its tip and fleets of lorries took the waste to a nearby landfill site instead. Some years earlier, Lewis Merthyr Colliery in South Wales installed a hopper to crush the stone to fist size and send it back down the

ABOVE: In 2013, the spoil heap of Yorkshire's Hatfield Colliery slipped and undermined an adjacent main line railway, throwing the tracks on to their side and closing the line for months. This incident should not be confused with subsidence (see next chapter).

mine, where it was either blown into the goaf by compressed air or mixed with concrete to help build the side walls of new roadways, but stowing the stone that way was an expensive and time-consuming process and didn't make financial sense for many mines. In fact, it could make the difference between a colliery being profitable or not, so most waste continued to be sent to the tips.

Britain's general switch from advance to retreat mining, in which the goaf did not need to be packed with stone for roof support, contributed to the increase in surface waste.

Colliery spoil has been used for various reasons in the past. Waste from Arkwright mine was used to fill a railway tunnel at Duckmanton, while Linby Colliery's was used to cover an entire disused railway marshalling yard at Annesley. Other tips have been landscaped or removed completely by bulldozers to remove an eyesore or reduce a danger.

The latter was the case in the small, quiet Welsh village of Aberfan after the dreadful 1966 tragedy described on page 95. ●

ROLLING COUNTRY!

NEAR the Staffordshire village of Himley is a pub whose patrons feel the effects of alcohol before they've even lifted a glass! It is the Crooked House and it's four feet lower on one side than the other.

The building was condemned in the 1940s but rescued by a brewery company, which used buttresses and girders to make it safe.

The inn's lopsided appearance is caused by mining subsidence dating back to the 1800s when one of its previous owners, Sir Stephen Glynne, ordered his men to remove more coal from deep beneath the building than was good for it. It is a graphic reminder of what can happen in the mining industry when things don't go to plan.

In most strata, the amount of subsidence is relatively predictable and as most undermined areas were in the countryside, damage was usually limited to cracks in farm buildings or collapsed drainage channels in fields. In those cases, the mining company paid compensation or undertook rectification, but it was inevitable that urban areas were affected too sometimes, especially with so many Victorian-era collieries having been located in urban areas.

The reason there were relatively few claims compared with the vast tonnages of coal removed over the centuries was due to the packing of worked-out areas with stone and other waste to help support the roof. Even with the more modern form of retreat mining, the worked-out void (the 'goaf') could be partially packed with stones before the roof was allowed to collapse, thus reducing the effect on the surface.

Where important buildings or strategic infrastructure such as railway lines were concerned, it was possible to prevent the situation by leaving unworked pillars of coal underneath them, but in former times, railway companies could purchase pillars of unworked coal under their property to prevent subsidence. Surprisingly, few did so, with the result that some routes were quite badly affected, the Leicester-Coalville line near the former Ellistown Colliery being a good example.

There was an unusual accident in January 1969 when a new loading bunker at Sharlston Colliery, Yorkshire, collapsed, destroying three British Rail wagons. The bunker had been built in the vicinity of an ancient mine shaft that had not shown up on old plans or been detected by preliminary boring.

That incident underlined the importance to the mining industry of surveyors. Theirs was one of the most important but underestimated departments in a mine. Not only did they keep the roadways and galleries going in the right direction but they

ABOVE: The effects of mining subsidence can be seen quite clearly in this view of the Coalville-Leicester line alongside the former Ellistown Colliery. Negotiating the dip at slow speed on February 6, 2015 are Type 1 diesel locos Nos. 20107, 20096, 20132 and 20118 working a brand-new London Underground train from Derby Works to a test centre established on the site of Asfordby Colliery, near Melton Mowbray. NICK PIGOTT

were responsible for knowing when the road-headers and coalface workers were due to pass beneath important surface locations, such as railways, roads and churches.

Most colliery offices or area headquarters had a surveyors' office where plans of underground workings were made and constantly updated.

Another important role of the surveyors was the charting of workings in areas where there was a likelihood of coal having been dug in an earlier century. This was to prevent miners suddenly breaking into a disused gallery or even plunging into one at a lower level, as actually happened on a few occasions. As it wasn't always possible to predict exactly where ancient workings were, test borings also had to be made to prevent breaking into a water-filled cavity.

An accidental breakthrough into the workings of a neighbouring mine could alter the ventilation flow of both collieries too, with possibly disastrous results for the men of both concerns.

Methods of surveying improved over the years, one way being for a seismic survey team to make small explosions on the ground. Based on the time it took the shock waves to travel through the earth, it was possible to tell what kind of rocks lay beneath.

Until 1942, when the state took legal ownership of coal and certain other mineral rights as a wartime measure, most owners of surface land owned the rights to what lay below, but that caused untold problems for colliery owners and their surveyors; the Wigan Coal Corporation, for instance, once had to negotiate with no fewer than 1,200 different landowners and lessors and deal with their relevant royalty claims in order to mine a coalfield or even make a simple extension to a roadway.

Fortunately for the advance of the industry, many coal owners in the early years were noblemen who were proprietors of colliery companies anyway, but just one refusal could cause problems for surveyors trying to plot straight roadways. ●

ABOVE: The potential risks of subsidence were at their worst in heavily built-up areas, as can be appreciated from this photograph of Bradford Colliery (which despite its name was in the heart of Manchester).

ABOVE: No, you've not been drinking! The Crooked House pub at Himley in Staffordshire really does lean at this drunken angle, a victim of ancient mining subsidence. NICK PIGOTT

TOO LITTLE AIR,
TOO MUCH WATER

ABOVE: As breathing apparatus became more reliable during the late Victorian era, rescue teams were set up to serve the larger or gassier collieries. This one was based at Mauchline Colliery in Ayrshire in the 1950s. Note the canary cage with its own miniature oxygen tank for reviving the bird if necessary!

VENTILATION sounds a straight-forward enough subject, but it was one of the most important aspects of mining operation – if not the most important.

Air didn't just serve the vital purpose of keeping miners alive by supplying fresh oxygen; it also performed the vital role of removing methane, carbon dioxide and coal dust from the atmosphere as well as partly compensating for the high levels of heat generated in the bowels of the earth.

Too little ventilation and those problems would all occur; too much ventilation and there was a risk in some mines of creating an environment conducive to spontaneous combustion.

The upcast and downcast air-circulation principle dates back to the days when bellpits began to be knocked through into each other and it was noticed that this had the effect of improving the strength and freshness of the flow, particularly when one shaft was deeper than the other.

In the early years of simple underground layouts, air ran through the galleries on its way from one shaft to the other, but that meant that the men working at the far end of the mine received foul air, so mines were divided into districts by the use of air doors to ensure that different sections of mine all received similar amounts of fresh air. The need for the doors was because the air would otherwise take the shortest route from one shaft to another, leaving all other parts of the mine unventilated.

To create a draught for ventilation in the early years, a furnace would be lit at the bottom of the upcast shaft and the hot air from it would rise, causing the air from the downcast shaft to follow it via the mine's various roadways and gateways. The problem with furnaces, of course, was that they created a large naked flame underground – the last thing needed with methane in the offing – so they were eventually phased out in favour of powerful fans, sadly not before several fatal blasts had occurred.

EXPLOSION

Fans capable of circulating 200,000 cubic feet per minute began to replace furnaces after 207 people died in the Blantyre explosion of October 22, 1877. It is thought that the ventilation furnace might have gone out overnight, causing air levels to fluctuate and allowing gas to build up. Ventilation sometimes causes blasts of cool (fresh) air and warm (exhaust) air to meet at underground junctions, providing an odd experience for anyone passing between one flow and another. At points where there was a chance of the two flows mixing or short-circuiting, air crossovers were installed.

Air pressure and speed in some mines was so great that the ventilation doors would be almost impossible to open, so a small regulator flap was sometimes positioned in the main door to help equalise the pressure and make it easier to open. To stop air passing into disused roadways, a 'stopping' was used to basically seal off the entrance.

The importance of proper ventilation was underlined at Wharncliff Woodmoor Colliery on August 6, 1936 when two airway doors were wedged open with bricks to facilitate the passage of tubs. That allowed firedamp to accumulate, which was then detonated by an electrical fault, resulting in an explosion that claimed the lives of 58 miners.

Dangerous levels of methane and heat could build up inside a mine if ventilation was switched off for any length of time, so fans, as well as water pumps where necessary, had to be kept running during long strikes and other periods of inactivity.

Today, the preserved Big Pit at Blaenafon is a good place to see powerful ventilation fans in action.

WATER: As mentioned in previous chapters, many lives were lost in mines as a result of water. This could either pour from subterranean watercourses or from abandoned mine workings and the battle to keep flooding at bay was a constant one that taxed the ingenuity of the early mining engineers.

Water percolating from the upper measures was often pure enough to drink and some mines collected it in lodgements at the shaft side and sold it to the local water authority, Whitwick Colliery in Leicestershire being an example. On the other hand, some mines had problems with toxic water leeching into watercourses and there were bodies like the South Yorkshire Mines Drainage Board, whose sole occupation was to keep pits dry. In 1943, that board installed the first submersible pump, which could be left to work unattended. Such machinery became very widespread in later years.

Water occurs naturally in the sub-strata and some pits simply had reputations for wetness right to the end of their lives; Westoe, for instance, had to have five-and-a-half million gallons of water pumped out every day and Northern United mine in Gloucestershire was raising 60 tons of water for every ton of coal when it closed in 1965. There was so much pressure from water in the Kent coalfield that the shafts of Snowdown Colliery began to collapse within days of the pumps being switched off following the mine's closure in 1987.

● Not all water was unwanted, of course. In the form of a fine spray, it played important roles in the laying of dust and the cooling of powerful cutting tools. Care had to be taken not to use excessive water as that would turn the dust underfoot into a morass of grey slurry similar to the cloying conditions on any colliery surface whenever it rained heavily. ●

When a 'tweet' meant Life or Death

IN 1913, Scottish physiologist John Haldane – who had investigated tragedies in which colliers had been poisoned by gas because they'd had no warning of its presence – came up with the idea of placing canaries in coal mines.

He reasoned that the faster metabolism and greater sensitivity of the birds (seven times more so than humans) would mean them becoming sick well before the men, thus giving them time to escape or at least put on respirators.

Aviaries were installed at collieries and a caged canary became an essential part of underground equipment. It was necessary to keep the birds' claws trimmed, however, as rigor-mortis could sometimes keep dead ones on their perches!

ABOVE: The canary cage at Littleton Colliery in 1993. NICK PIGOTT

TOO MANY WAYS TO DIE

EVERY day, underground men went to work not knowing if they would return home that night. They faced death in numerous different ways.

To stress just how many ways a mineworker could perish, be crippled or become permanently ill, the main causes are listed below:
• Roof fall
• Shaft plunge
• Explosion of methane
• Explosion of coal dust
• Subterranean fire
• Subterranean flood
• Suffocation
• Train or tub accident
• Cage over-wind
• Pneumoconiosis

Until the horrors of the two world wars led people in western society to reappraise the sanctity of human life, many industrial proprietors viewed their workers as dispensible means to an end and injury, mutilation and death were almost daily occurrences in mining communities.

The statistics speak for themselves. In the 30 years between 1880 and 1910, there were more than 1,000 fatalities a year in British coal mines – an average of three men killed every day.

In 1910 the national fatality figure for the year rose to a shocking 1,818. Of those, 501 died in explosions, 658 in roof or wall falls, 286 in accidents involving the transport of coal underground and 373 as a result of other types of misfortune. Injuries totalled 173,700 that dreadful year – an average of 470 a day!

The first recorded victim of a coal mining accident in Britain appears to have been a man by the name of Ralf Ulger, who drowned while digging for sea coal in 1243 and although there would have been numerous fatalities after that, the first recorded death of an underground collier appears to be that of James Townend, who was killed in a firedamp explosion at Barnsley in 1672.

The last three men to die in British deep mines were all Kellingley victims, who died between 2008 and 2011. One was Don Cook, whose mother summed up the remarkable affection in which colliers viewed their perilous jobs when she commented afterwards: "He loved being a miner. It's a wonderful culture and a wonderful life."

The last subterranean coal mining tragedy of all in the UK occurred on September 15, 2011 at Gleision Colliery, a small private drift mine at Cilybebyll, near Rhos in South Wales. Although checked regularly by the Mines Inspectorate, it was in some respects operated in conditions reminiscent of the Victorian era. There had been an inrush of water and debris, trapping four men, all of whom perished 300ft underground.

The **Worst Tragedies** in British Mining History

440 died at Senghenydd, Wales, in 1913
371 at Oaks Colliery, Yorkshire, 1866
344 at Pretoria Pit, Lancashire, 1910
294 Albion Colliery, Cilfynydd, 1894
268 Prince of Wales, Abercarn, 1878
265 Gresford, near Wrexham, 1934
207 Blantyre, Lanarkshire, 1877
204 Hartley, Northumberland, 1862
189 Lundhill, near Wombwell 1857
189 Wood Pit, Haydock, Lancs, 1878
178 Clifton Hall, Lancs, 1885
178 Ferndale, Glamorgan, 1867
176 Llanerch, Monmouthshire, 1890
168 West Stanley, Co Durham, 1909
164 Seaham, Co Durham, 1880
155 Minie Pit, Staffordshire, 1918
143 Swaithe Main, Barnsley 1875
142 Black Vein, Risca, 1860
139 Combs, Dewsbury, Yorkshire, 1893
136 Wellington, Whitehaven 1910
120 Black Vein, Risca (2nd tragedy), 1880
119 Wattstown, Glamorgan, 1905
114 Cynmer, Glamorgan, 1856
112 Parc Slip, Glamorgan, 1892
104 William Pit, Whitehaven, 1947
102 Wallsend, Northumberland 1835
101 Penycraig, Glamorgan, 1880

In addition, 144 lives (116 children and 28 adults) were lost in October 1966 when a 40ft high pile of slurry slid off a spoil heap and engulfed Pantglas Junior School in Aberfan, South Wales (see page 95). NB. Almost half the above disasters occurred in Wales.

The overall total of miners killed in the UK between 1851 and 2015 is close to 100,000 – but even taking the comparatively accident-free second half of the 20th century into account, the figure has to be seen in the context of a vast workforce numbering at its peak almost one-and-a-quarter-million men spread over 3,000 collieries.

Probably the most famous person to die in a coal mine was international footballer Walter Bennett, who won two caps for England while playing for top First Division club Sheffield United in 1901. He was killed in a roof fall at Denaby Main Colliery in April 1908. In those days, even international players' earnings were insufficient to let them retire and he'd had to take a job in the pits after hanging up his boots.

The Lundhill disaster of 1859 and others at that time appealed to the unhealthy Victorian tendency for sightseers to flock to the scene; thousands of 'excursionists' arriving by train from non-mining areas and creating something of a country

ABOVE: Flames shoot from the ventilation outlet at Lundhill Colliery, where 189 men lost their lives in an explosion in 1857.

ABOVE: How the *Daily Herald* broke the news of the Wharncliffe Woodmoor Colliery tragedy near Barnsley in August 1936.

ABOVE: This graphic artist's interpretation of an underground explosion is a well-known one in mining circles and says far more about the potential horror of life in the pits than a photograph ever could.

fair atmosphere rather than one of mourning at a scene of great human suffering.

The Oaks Colliery explosion at Ardsley in 1866 was Britain's largest peacetime disaster since the Great Fire of London 200 years earlier. The bodies of more than 100 men remain entombed to this day. One of the blasts sent a cage shooting up its shaft and into the headgear. The flames eventually had to be extinguished by stopping up the shafts to starve them of oxygen. A total of 371 men and youths perished, including 27 members of the rescue team. Some of the survivors found jobs at other mines but by a cruel twist of fate, one of them was killed in a roof fall near Barnsley four years later.

The worst disaster of all in British coal mining history occurred at Senghenydd, in South Wales, in October 1913, when 440 people perished (see panel).

Some examples of the different forms of death that lay in wait for mineworkers are as follows:

Roof fall: At Bilsthorpe Colliery in August 1993, a block of sandstone said to be the size of a small asteroid and weighing 8,000 tons, fell from a roof into a roadway, destroying the pit props (they were never intended to withstand such a colossal weight) and killing three men working underneath.

It was one of the largest single falls, but it was typical of the incidents with which miners have had to contend for centuries.

So many roof falls took place, especially in the early years of mining, that there were hardly any collieries that didn't have at least one such episode in their histories and the memorial gardens at Senghenydd are a sobering reminder of this fact, with hundreds of stone plaques paying tribute to all the serious

mining accidents that have rocked the principality over the decades.

Given the phenomenal volume of earth and rock above every subterranean gallery, it is a remarkable testament to the skill of the engineers and miners that so (relatively) few

major roof fall tragedies have occurred when it is considered how many hundreds of years mining has been undertaken in Britain.

The risk of roof falls remained a feature of mining right up until the end of the industry: At Hatfield Colliery in the 21st century, health & safety men still drilled 'telltale' measuring devices into the roadway walls and roofs every 20 metres, in districts where the risk was highest, to detect any movement in the rock.

Shaft plunge: One of the most horrible ways to die was in a cage that was either plummeting downwards or shooting upwards too fast to stop; the occupants knew what was happening and could only wait for the inevitable.

In 1886, an appalling accident occurred at Houghton Main Colliery, Barnsley, when a cage containing 10 men plummeted to the bottom of a 535yd shaft in just 12 seconds at a speed of more than 100mph. It splintered into smithereens as it smashed into the sump at the bottom of the shaft.

At Rufford Colliery, near Mansfield, in 1913, there was a terrible incident when a winding engineman was temporarily unsighted by a tarpaulin sheet that fell on him while he was raising a seven-ton tank of water in one of the cages. Without his hand at ▶

The **Biggest Catastrophe** of them all

BY far the worst of all Britain's mining disasters occurred at Universal Colliery in Senghenydd, near Caerphilly, on October 14, 1913, when an underground explosion claimed the lives of 439 miners.

Many collieries on the South Wales coalfield mined seams that contained high quantities of methane ('firedamp') and Universal was no exception. It had already suffered an extremely serious incident 12 years earlier when three underground explosions killed 81 men.

The cause of the 1913 catastrophe was never established for sure but almost certainly related to the high levels of airborne dust for which the colliery was notorious. An initial methane blast, probably caused by a spark, is likely to have been carried further into the workings of the mine by a chain reaction of explosions.

Those men not killed instantly died as a result of inhaling afterdamp, a poisonous mixture of carbon dioxide, carbon monoxide and nitrogen left after an explosion.

Fire in the workings hampered rescue efforts and it took six weeks for most of the bodies to be recovered and the blaze to be extinguished. One rescuer died in the process, taking the death toll to 440.

ABOVE: Long lines of miners and their loved ones queue up at Senghenydd Colliery to wait for news following Britain's worst mining disaster in 1913.

In 1981, a memorial was unveiled in the village, followed by a second in 2006 to honour the dead of the 1901 and 1913 Universal Colliery explosions. On the centenary of the main tragedy in 2013, a memorial to 152 of Wales's worst mining tragedies was unveiled, featuring a bronze statue of a rescue worker helping a survivor.

LEFT: The Prince of Wales takes a moment to reflect after laying a wreath at the Welsh mining memorial at Senghenydd in 2014.

ABOVE: At Scotland's Barony Colliery in 1962, an entire winding tower collapsed into the top of its own shaft. Thankfully such incidents were extremely rare. NCB

ABOVE AND BELOW: Selections of safety lamps can be seen in all mining museums and demonstrate the remarkable variety since the early 19th century.

the controls, the tank hit the headgear, broke loose and plunged back down the shaft. Fourteen men working near the bottom were killed by the force of the water and flying metal as the tank shattered.

In 1915, two cages at Bentinck Colliery, Notts, collided at the halfway point at a combined speed of 80mph.

The wooden floor of the descending cage was displaced by the impact and seven men fell 660ft to their deaths. Two more died of injuries sustained in the collision and some of the survivors were left dangling, one of them upside down suspended by his trousers, which had luckily snagged on a piece of metal. So mutilated were some of the bodies at

the foot of the shaft that relatives had difficulty identifying them.

Suffocation and gas poisoning: Miners' lives were plagued by several different types of poisonous or asphyxiating gases that could be found in pits. The names of these were all characterised by the suffix 'damp' (a derivation of the German word 'dampf', meaning vapour).

Blackdamp (also known as Chokedamp): A mixture of carbon dioxide and nitrogen that could cause suffocation and oxygen deficiency. It is odourless and colourless and gained its name from the fact that lights wouldn't burn in it and hence darkness ensued.

Whitedamp: A toxic, odourless residual gas consisting primarily of carbon monoxide and so called because (unlike blackdamp), it allows lights to continue burning. To detect it, miners took caged canaries underground (see panel on page 89).

Stinkdamp, so called because its principal content was hydrogen sulphide (which smells of rotten eggs). Unlike odourless methane, it was easily detected but was extremely poisonous. It might seem trivial, but miners were reluctant to pack egg sandwiches in their lunchboxes for fear it would mask, or be mistaken for, the smell of stinkdamp.

Afterdamp: a poisonous cocktail of carbon monoxide, carbon dioxide, nitrogen, hydrogen, oxygen and residual

Illness and **Disease**

MINERS did not only have to face a multitude of injury hazards during the course of their careers; also stalking them constantly were illnesses and diseases.

Many afflictions were peculiar to the mining industry and were found in few other walks of life – nystagmus for instance – a strange ailment that resulted in a rapid involuntary oscillation of the eyeballs and which was caused by working in poor light over many years.

The most notorious and widely known disease was pneumoconiosis (the miners' dreaded 'Black Lung'). One has only to look at photographs of miners with black faces to realise how much coal dust must have been passing into their mouths and nostrils.

When underground in a colliery, the beam of a cap lamp would pick up thousands of tiny shimmering particles of coal suspended in the air – even in a well-ventilated modern mine and not even at the coalface.

Although many such particles were prevented from being inhaled and swallowed by the natural action of the nose and throat, those that did get through to the lungs caused minute scarring and clogged up the tiny air pockets in the lung tissue, causing a slow lingering death for many thousands of older men.

Not all miners contracted pneumoconiosis, just as not all smokers contract lung cancer, but to help combat the problem, dust masks and other safety measures were implemented for underground workers in the 1970s. Water sprinklers were also introduced to help suppress the dust and to damp it down at most points at which coal was transferred from one conveyor to another. As a result, pneumoconiosis is almost unknown among younger ex-miners.

Colliers suffered terribly from lung diseases – but even worse off were their colleagues whose job it was to drive headings through solid rock to open up new roadways. They were constantly breathing stone dust, but because that type of work meant that they were

continuously moving from colliery to colliery, they were never at one mine very long. This enabled less caring coal owners to deny that the disease, called silicosis, had been contracted on their premises. As a consequence, the men were unable to gain compensation and had to rely on parish funds to see out their final years. In later years, face masks were supplied for road-header operators.

Other afflictions faced by miners were emphysema, bronchitis and 'white finger', which was caused by vibration and particularly affected men who cut coal from the face with hand-held power tools driven by compressed air or electricity.

In 2001, there were 19,000 outstanding compensation cases of white finger waiting to be resolved, along with 14,500 cases of emphysema and bronchitis, and 4,000 cases of deafness brought about by the noise of powerful machinery in confined spaces.

Of course, there were also the many other conditions associated with heavy manual work – bad backs and ruptures from heavy lifting, inflammation of the joints, head injuries in the days before helmets and so on... but there was also an ailment peculiar to miners called 'beat knee', which was caused by spending year after year crawling or kneeling on jagged surfaces. 'Beat hand' was another recognised condition.

One aspect that is not so widely known outside pit communities is that some older miners bore tiny dark blue scars on their nose and forehead and carried them to their deaths. This was due to coal dust entering little cuts and abrasions without them realising it. As the new skin grew under the scab it formed a blue stain like a tattoo.

Despite all the disadvantages listed above, coal dust was credited by many miners with great healing powers. It was rubbed into wounds and grazes and some men also sucked lumps of coal to ease thirst. Many others ingested large quantities of it over the years simply by eating their sandwiches and suchlike in dusty atmospheres, yet still lived to a ripe old age.

The Constant need for **Safety**

A MINER'S safety underground depended on the man next to him and that constant need for vigilance and loyalty – even with colleagues they might not have particularly got on with above ground – formed a vital bond and a sense of camaraderie that ran through their lives. Miners had to trust one another and individualism and indiscipline were effectively outlawed by the very nature of the task.

The first official rescue station was initiated in 1902 and Central Rescue Stations, within 10 miles of every mine, were made compulsory under the Coal Mines Regulation Act of 1911.

SAFETY LAMPS: Under law, a man with at least the qualification of a Deputy was required to check methane and carbon dioxide levels every one-and-a-half hours, using a safety lamp adjacent to any area where men were working. Methane makes a lamp's flame burn blue and change shape the more methane is present. Carbon dioxide, which is heavier than air, makes the flame go out through absence of oxygen.

Methane is only explosive between 2.2% and 4% mixed with air, so when the methane level was less than 2.2%, it was safe not only for miners to work but for otherwise lethally dangerous activities such as explosive shot-firing to take place.

Although it became possible in recent years to detect firedamp and other gases by electronic means, miners continued to be equipped with safety lamps right up until the very last day of deep mining in Britain in 2015. Unless a colliery was classified as a naked light mine (a category that was done away with by the NCB in the 1950s), all electrical equipment underground had by law to be flameproof or 'intrinsically safe' to reduce the chances of a spark igniting a patch of methane gas.

In the modern era, intrinsically safe equipment meant low-power apparatus such as self-powered telephones, signalling equipment or low-voltage cameras that were incapable of generating an incendive spark.

SELF-RESCUERS: Even in the best-regulated modern mines, the threat from fire or gas remained ever present, so self-rescuer apparatus was introduced in 1960 following a number of fires in which men were killed by inhalation of fumes.

Self-rescuers were portable kits clipped to the belt of every underground worker. There were two basic types; one that generated oxygen and one that used a filter to remove carbon monoxide, the latter type being the most common in British mines. By means of a mask and nose-clip, they provided breathable air for about an hour, which gave most men a fighting chance of getting back to the surface provided they weren't too many miles from the shaft bottom when the emergency occurred.

CAGE ARRESTORS: Following a high number of cage over-wind incidents in which men had been killed or maimed, Nottinghamshire man John King invented the King patent detaching hook in 1860. In the event of an over-wind by an engine man at either end of a shaft, a hook would engage with the headgear, suspending the cage and releasing the rope.

In the event of steam pressure falling too low in a winding house boiler, a solenoid with counter-balance weights would drop and automatically apply a caliper brake to stop the engine.

From 1917, headstocks had by law to be fitted with over-wind mechanisms, but most colliery managers still insisted on the winding engine men being able to concentrate fully on the job in hand and it was often the case that his cabin would be kept locked to prevent colleagues from entering without permission.

KEEPING A TALLY: The official death toll in the coal dust explosion at Blantyre in 1877 was 207 but the actual figure is thought to have been higher because no proper check had been taken of who had gone underground that morning. This lax state of affairs was later addressed by the compulsory issuing of numbered discs or triangles known as 'tallies' to all workers before they entered a shaft or drift.

Each miner was issued with a personal pit number, which would be kept for the duration of his time at that colliery and would be engraved or fitted on to his safety lamp and on to two brass tallies (sometimes known as 'checks'). The miner would hand one tally to the banksman at the top of the shaft and retain the other with its matching number while underground. He would then hand it to the banksman as he stepped out of the cage at the end of his shift. By counting the tallies and lamps given out each day, the lamphouse staff knew which men were down a mine at any given time.

A similar system is still used today for construction workers going down into the Crossrail tunnels in central London, but in that respect they are not as advanced as Kellingley Colliery, which in a last belated concession to modernity replaced its brass check system with a 21st century card swipe machine at the pithead shortly before the mine closed.

---

methane left in the atmosphere of a mine after an explosion of either firedamp or coal dust. It is not flammable itself but, depending on circumstances, has been known to kill more miners in the aftermath of an explosion than the blast itself.

Firedamp: Last but by no means least, this was the most common form of 'damp'. It comprises a highly combustible mixture of gases, the principal one of which is methane.

Methane is lighter than air and tends to accumulate in roof cavities. It is not poisonous but was the cause of thousands of mining deaths over the years due to its flammability.

The first recorded death in Britain from a methane gas explosion was in Durham in 1621, but miners continued to use candles, oil lamps and other naked flames for two more centuries.

Until the invention of safety lamps, there was little option but to rid the

mine of methane by deliberately igniting it. For that job, a 'fireman' wearing a monk-like hood and thick water-soaked clothing would gingerly crawl forward with a naked light on the end of a long stick, keeping his head down so that the blast would hopefully pass over him, but jumping up immediately afterwards to avoid breathing the low-lying afterdamp. As can be imagined, people did not last very long in that job!

Don't go down in the mine, **Dad**

A mining disaster in South Wales in 1907 inspired lyricists Robert Donnely and Will Geddes to compose the following, published in 1910.

A miner was leaving his home for his work,
When he heard his little child scream;
He went to his bedside, his little white face,
"Oh, Daddy, I've had such a dream;
I dreamt that I saw the pit all afire,
And men struggled hard for their lives;
The scene it then changed, and the top of the mine
Was surrounded by sweethearts and wives."

Chorus:
Don't go down in the mine, Dad,
Dreams very often come true;
Daddy, you know it would break my heart
If anything happened to you;
Just go and tell my dream to your mates,
And as true as the stars that shine,
Something is going to happen today,
Dear Daddy, don't go down the mine!

The miner, a man with a heart good and kind,
Stood by the side of his son;
He said, "It's my living, I can't stay away,
For duty, my lad, must be done."
The little one look'd up, and sadly he said,
"Oh, please stay today with me, Dad!"
But as the brave miner went forth, to his work,
He heard this appeal from his lad:

Repeat chorus.

Whilst waiting his turn with his mates to descend,
He could not banish his fears,
He return'd home again to his wife and his child,
Those words seem'd to ring through his ears,
And, ere the day ended, the pit was on fire,
When a score of brave men lost their lives;
He thank'd God above for the dream his child had
As once more the little one cries:

Repeat chorus.

Between 1813 and 1815, several designs of safety lamp were devised by the likes of William Clanny, Humphry Davy and George Stephenson. These not only provided safe (if dim) illumination but also showed whether methane was present. If it was, the shape and colour of the flame would change. The Davy lamp, in which the flame was contained behind a gauze screen, became the best known and over the ensuing years, the efficiency of the various designs of lamps improved tremendously, not only saving lives but making it possible for millions of tons of otherwise unrecoverable coal to be mined.

Sparks from pick-axes could potentially cause a methane explosion too, as could shot-firing, wiring faults and overheated machinery. Low barometric pressure encouraged methane to issue from the strata, exacerbating the risk.

Depending on the type of seam it is trapped in, methane is usually emitted at a known rate, which, while not eradicating the dangers, made risk assessment at any given colliery easier to manage. Statistically, the most dangerous seam in Britain was the Hutton seam in the Great Northern coalfield, which caused 37 explosions and killed 1,090 people between 1705 and 1883.

Explosion of coal dust: If there were large quantities of coal dust in the air at the time of a methane blast, a series of chain reaction explosions could be triggered and tear along the whole length of a roadway, killing men far away from the source of the first blast. The burning of coal dust also creates poisonous carbon monoxide, which also resulted in deaths. In the 1870s, such a series of explosions killed 73 men at Udston Colliery, Hamilton. It was a dry, dusty pit and after that it became compulsory to liberally scatter limestone dust all over underground walls and roadways as it was found that it had a preventative effect by diluting the concentration of coal dust. Shelves containing limestone dust were also placed across the top of the roadways at strategic locations. The force of the blast would blow the limestone dust off the shelves and snuff out the chain reaction.

This practice was continued until the end of deep mining in 2015 and is still carried out today at the preserved Blaenafon Colliery.

Subterranean fire: In addition to the many fires caused by methane explosions, blazes could result from other sources. In 1950, for example, a conveyor belt in the main air intake roadway at Cresswell Colliery jammed and the resultant friction caused it to overheat and burst into flames, the rubber producing thick acrid smoke that trapped 80 miners. They all died of carbon monoxide poisoning. The roadway was sealed off as the only means of starving the fire of oxygen while keeping the rest of the pit operational, but several men did not go to work the next day as a mark of respect - a long-standing tradition in the mining industry.

The cause of the jammed belt was later found to have been extremely lax maintenance and fault-reporting methods, coupled with poorly maintained fire extinguishers and water supply. It proved to be a watershed in mine safety, bringing about introduction of a 'self-rescuer' breathing mask.

Some miners' trains could be 300ft long and in the days before radio communication, several men died when their train was being propelled (rather than hauled) towards a coalface. Unbeknown to the driver at the rear, a fire had broken out near the face and his passengers were being choked to death by thick smoke. The guard at the front had no way of telling the driver at the rear to stop. By the time the driver realised what was happening and began hauling the train out, it was too late for those at the front. Safety improvements implemented as a result brought about changes in train operation.

Spontaneous combustion: It may seem strange that a fire - which requires oxygen in order to burn - can survive underground, but in fact some subterranean conflagrations have been burning continuously for more than half a century, defying all man's ingenuity to extinguish them. In Germany, there is said to be a coal seam fire that has been smouldering since 1668 despite numerous attempts to extinguish it.

Such phenomena are caused by natural spontaneous combustion and although serious outbreaks were relatively rare in Britain, they were most prevalent in the thick seams of Staffordshire, Warwickshire and South Derbyshire.

The most recent in the UK broke out in the workings of Warwickshire's Daw Mill Colliery in 2013, doing so much damage underground that the mine had to close - a nevertheless controversial decision for such a productive pit.

The usual ways of combating an underground blaze were either to starve it of oxygen by sealing it off, to flood the mine, as happened at Hucknall in 1867, or (in more recent times) to pump large quantities of the inert gas nitrogen into the workings. The latter method, however, is prohibitively expensive.

Subterranean flooding: The Lofthouse Colliery disaster occurred in 1973 when water burst through a seam and trapped seven men 750ft underground. Rescue teams worked out where the men were estimated to be and set up a drilling rig on the surface above that point to bore an air hole for them while frogmen from the NCB's underwater rescue team based at Hednesford, Staffs, tried to reach them. So heavy was the inundation that it took six days before the first body could be retrieved and all hope for the other six was then abandoned. They are entombed to this day.

The funeral and memorial service was conducted by the Bishop of Wakefield, the Rt Rev Eric Treacy, a renowned industrial enthusiast who would often visit his parishioners in the collieries and crawl on his belly through very thin seams to reach those working at the coalface.

Crushing by trains and machines: A surprisingly high number of deaths and serious injuries have been caused by train derailments and by runaway mine cars either pinning men against other tubs, or trapping them against walls in narrow roadways.

A fatal crash occurred at Silverwood Colliery in 1966 when a train of materials crashed into the rear of a passenger-carrying train, killing 10 miners and seriously injuring 29 others.

Seven men were killed and 19 injured at Bentley Colliery, Doncaster, in 1978 when a train ran away down an underground incline. After that, speed retarders were fitted to the tracks in most mines.

In 1991, there was an unusual accident at Thurcroft Colliery when a conveyor on which men were riding suddenly began to speed up due to a faulty gearbox. As it reached speeds of 40mph, panic set in and lots of men jumped off, sustaining serious injuries and broken bones as a result of being

Searching for 'Contraband'

WHY could a miner take a Mars bar underground but not a KitKat? The first was permitted, the second prohibited.

It was all to do with the foil wrapping around the chocolate, for anything that could generate a spark was classed as 'contraband'. So strictly was this rule enforced that the pit canteen staff would not sell a miner a meat pie to put in his 'snap' (lunch) tin unless they first removed it from its foil container. It might come as a surprise to some readers, but under certain conditions even dried orange peel could generate a spark.

In view of the above, it almost goes without saying that matches and cigarettes were forbidden, although snuff and chewing tobacco were allowed.

Despite the obvious dangers, some miners still tried to smuggle fags and similar suspect items underground, secreted among their clothing. In 1959, a miner at Moorgreen Colliery was sent to jail for smoking underground, so large signs at the pithead reminded men to check their pockets before entering the cage.

Wide-ranging powers were given to the banksmen in charge of the cages, allowing them to make airport-style body searches to check for contraband at any time they wanted.

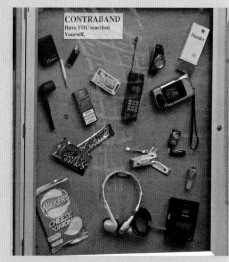

ABOVE: This example of what miners were forbidden to take underground was on display at Snibston Colliery until its closure to the public in 2015.

thrown against steel girders and roof supports. More than 40 had to be taken to hospital in a fleet of ambulances.

Other injuries: In 1950 alone, there were 11,058 notifiable eye injuries in mining, yet remarkably, it wasn't until 1972 that the Protection of Eyes Regulations were introduced. All that was in addition to conditions caused by having to work for years in poor light. ●

The Aberfan **Disaster**

ONE of the worst and most poignant mining tragedies didn't kill a single miner.

At 9.15am on October 21, 1966, the pupils of Pantglas Junior School in Aberfan were just about to start lessons when the entire building was buried under thousands of tons of waterlogged coal and shale slurry that slid down from an adjacent spoil tip without warning.

A total of 144 people died, 116 of them children aged between seven and 10.

The deputy head teacher, Mr Beynon, was found dead clutching five children in his arms as if he had been protecting them.

A nearby farm and row of terraced cottages were also engulfed and several adults perished in those buildings.

Miners from local mines, especially the one that had produced the tip – Merthyr Vale Colliery – left their jobs to help the 2,000-strong rescue team dig for survivors, but largely in vain.

It was later found that the tip had been destabilised by a spring that flowed beneath it and the National Coal Board was blamed by the official inquiry for extreme negligence in allowing it to be built over the spring despite earlier warnings from villagers. The heap was later removed as a safety precaution and many similar tips – incorrectly referred to almost universally by the national media as 'slag heaps' – began to be landscaped or at least lowered in height, so as not to pose such a threat to surrounding buildings. Some of those left in the 'middle of nowhere' following demolition of their parent colliery were left in situ but planted with trees or grass to blend into the countryside.

Today, a memorial garden stands on the site of the Aberfan school and the bodies of the children, their teachers and the other victims lie in the village's cemetery, their graves marked by a long row of special white arches visible right across the valley.

ABOVE AND BELOW: On October 21, 1966, the spoil tip of Merthyr Vale Colliery slid down on to the village of Aberfan, engulfing a primary school and killing 144 people, 116 of them children. Today, their short lives are recalled in moving fashion by the sight of this teddy bear at the Welsh National Mining Memorial at Senghenydd and by these lovingly maintained graves in Aberfan cemetery.

NO **SMOKING!**

LEFT: It is somewhat ironic that the plants that produced smokeless fuel were some of the smokiest and steamiest themselves… although that stands to reason as the volatile components had to be removed before reaching the consumer. This scene at the now-closed Glasshoughton works in 1970 shows Robert Stephenson & Hawthorn fireless locomotive No. 8082 – believed to be the last everyday working example of a lineage of Stephenson locos that began in the early 1800s. BRIAN SHARPE

The coke industry in Britain began as far back as the 16th century when bituminous coal was heated in earth mounds laid on the ground. When the process was improved in the 1700s by the introduction of dome-shaped brick ovens, the name 'beehive' was coined and at one time there were tens of thousands of such structures dotted across the nation's coalfields. A major breakthrough came in 1709 when industrialist Abraham Darby discovered that coke could be used instead of charcoal in the smelting of ore to produce iron – a major factor in the lead-up to the Industrial Revolution.

By the 1840s, railways were being built all over Britain and with thousands of trains running every day, it was becoming impractical and expensive for coal to have to be converted into coke in order to keep emissions low, so once the fireboxes of locomotives began to be fitted with brick arches to burn off excess gases, the 'consumption' law was quietly forgotten.

The developing world was by then fully in the grip of the Industrial Revolution and the demand for iron and steel for construction and engineering was reaching phenomenal proportions, placing enormous strain on the nation's still rather rudimentary beehive ovens. It was by then becoming clear that tall vertical ovens made of cast iron and lined with refractory bricks would carbonise the coal more efficiently and plants of this design began to be

L ONG before it became better known as a popular soft drink, coke was a household name in Great Britain. In fact, some of the earliest railway locomotives burned it instead of coal following introduction of a law requiring steam engines "to consume their own smoke".

Coke is a hard, grey, porous substance formed by the baking of coal in an oven to drive off volatile matter, leaving a strong yet lightweight carbon-rich element suitable for burning in the blast furnaces of iron and steel plants.

It is also used as a smokeless fuel in homes and factories, which is heavily ironic… for the method by which it is produced was one of the smokiest imaginable and the pyrotechnic display at the discharge stage of the coke-making process is an astonishing visual spectacle never to be forgotten by anyone allowed to witness it at close quarters.

ABOVE: Early coke ovens were shaped like beehives, hence their name.

ABOVE: Spacemen! Coke oven operatives today are required by regulations to wear protective clothing and helmets.

ABOVE: The awesome moment at which the incandescent coke is pushed out of the oven and into the waiting coke wagon is one that no one who ever witnesses it could ever forget. Such sights were still possible at Scunthorpe's Dawes Lane coke ovens until closure of the plant in March 2016. NICK PIGOTT

ABOVE AND LEFT: There are four types of railed vehicle at a typical coking plant. Two of them – the guide car and the coke wagon – can be seen in the above picture. The others are the charge car (above), which runs along the top of the ovens and is rarely seen, and the huge pusher vehicle (left), which runs along the back of the batteries.

built during the last two decades of the Victorian era.

The new ovens were arranged side-by-side in the form of massive 'batteries' baking coal around the clock and lighting up the night sky with an orange glow as their incandescent products were removed from the ovens and quenched with water to cool them down.

Several by-products are produced during the carbonisation process – notably gas, tar, benzole, coal-oil and ammonia. In earlier centuries, these would have been allowed to escape to the atmosphere or be dumped as waste, but it was then found that the gas could be captured and stored for domestic and street-lighting purposes. The coal-oil was used to produce aviation fuel for the Royal Air Force during the Second World War and since then commercial

uses have been developed for all the other by-products too, improving the environment and resulting in a surprisingly varied selection of household products produced either directly or indirectly, such as soap, aspirin, nylon and even perfume.

At one time, by-product coking plants were the most complicated refractory structures built by man and the coalfields and steelworks of Britain possessed almost 200 of them, converting between them a staggering 30million tons of coal a year into coke at the height of the industry's influence midway through the 20th century. When the Bolsover plant opened in Derbyshire just before the Second World War, it was the largest of its type in the entire world.

The last of the old beehive ovens in Britain were closed in 1958 and an

indication of just how extensively the country's heavy industry has been destroyed since then is that even their efficient replacements have been almost totally eradicated. There are now only two left - one at Appleby in Scunthorpe and the other at Morfa, near Port Talbot in South Wales.

Until December 2014, there were half a dozen of these huge structures still in operation (including the last independent commercial plant at Monckton, Yorkshire), but that and three steelworks-owned ones were shut down between then and March 2016, primarily as a result of competition from cheap Chinese imports.

The latest casualty has been the Dawes Lane complex in Scunthorpe, which was one of the country's biggest with 75 large ovens arranged in three batteries. Each chamber was ▶

approximately 50ft long, 18ft high and 3ft wide, and at its peak the plant was capable of producing more than a million tons of coke a year for the North Lincolnshire town's blast furnaces.

Of course, coke isn't used only in steelworks. There are three main grades, one for blast furnaces, one for foundries and one for factory and domestic use. With regard to the latter, readers of a certain age will recall its widespread use as a smokeless fuel, marketed under trade names such as Coalite in the days before gas-fired central heating became the rage. Following the Clean Air Act of 1956, smokeless zones began to be introduced in Britain and even in regions where they were not yet compulsory, young housewives hankered after the hot, low flame of modern coke stoves in place of smoky, labour-intensive coal fires.

That commercial aspect partly explains why many coking plants were attached to collieries, for the coke and the by-products generated profitable sidelines, including export trade markets.

So, how does a coking plant function? Every morning, laboratory technicians at Scunthorpe and Port Talbot analyse the day's blend of coals to ensure they have the characteristics required to make lumps of coke strong enough to support a 50ft column of ore, limestone and other substances in a blast furnace without collapsing under the weight. Coal is more brittle than coke, which is one of the reasons why it is not placed directly into the furnaces, the other being that it can lose much of its calorific value in fume emission before it fully ignites.

Not all types of coal are suitable for coking and the chemical analysis of the carbon, sulphur, moisture and ash content has become even more important since closure of Britain's last deep mines in 2015, for the coal now has to be transported from as far away as Columbia, Australia and Russia. As it happens, many foreign coals are lower in sulphur content than British types anyway, so result in better-quality iron and steel.

Buying in coking coal from abroad is not as new a phenomenon as might be imagined, for back in 1976, the chairman of the Coke Oven Managers Association revealed that it was "cheaper to import coal from Australia to Port Talbot than to move it by train from Staffordshire to Port Talbot!" He also pointed out that sea freight charges from America to west Wales were approximately the same as rail freight from east Wales!

Forty years later, the Scunthorpe and Port Talbot plants are buying in ready-made coke as well as coal, but (notwithstanding the pending sale of the plants) owner Tata Steel is investing in the Appleby plant to ensure that it can retain an element of self-sufficiency in a politically uncertain world.

Once it has been established that the day's supply of coal has a carbon content of at least 83 to 91%, it is taken from a coal-blending bunker, crushed and then charged by gravity into the top of the ovens (known in the industry as carbonising chambers). Each oven can contain about 30 tonnes of coal, which is heated by gas flues in an airtight, oxygen-free environment, allowing the fixed carbon and residual ash to fuse together to form the hard,

grey, porous coke. The moisture content and volatile crude vapours leave the chambers by 'ascension pipes' and are condensed and cleaned at the plant's chemical works to form the various by-products.

The old beehive ovens used to take 72 hours or more to carbonise the coal fully, but modern plants can do it in as little as 18 hours as they reach temperatures of well over 1,000C (1,832F). The plants are in operation day and night, all year round, even on Christmas Day, as the process cannot be slowed down or stopped without risking serious damage to the oven walls. As it is, the chambers have to be fired in a certain order to prevent the walls between them warping as a result of overly rapid cooling.

A typical coke works is served by four sets of rail lines. One set on the roof, along which a charge car runs in order to load the crushed coal into the ovens; one broad gauge set at the rear for the enormous pusher machine that literally pushes the red-hot coke out of the oven; and two at the front – one for a guide car and one for a locomotive-powered coke wagon. In all four cases, there is a spare vehicle on standby to ensure continuity in the production process.

When it is the time for an oven to be discharged, the guide car is

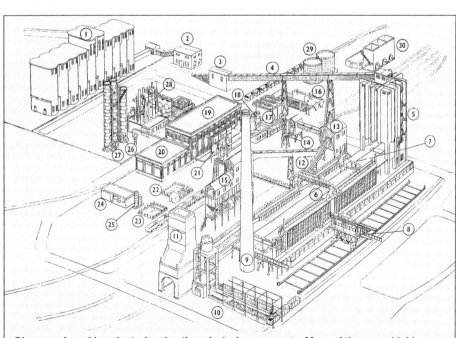

Diagram of a coking plant, showing the principal components. Many of those are highly technical in nature but the relevant ones are 1: Coal blending bunkers 2: Coal crusher house 6: Coke oven batteries 7: Charging car 8: Pusher machine 11: Coke quenching tower 13: Primary coke screens 24: Lime mixing station 27: Benzole scrubbers 28: Benzole plant 30: Water-cooling towers. (The coke car and guide car are not visible, being on the other side of the ovens).

ABOVE: At the Bolsover smokeless fuel plant in February 1993, freshly produced coke cools off in railway wagons before leaving the works. This plant, which was sandwiched between Bolsover and Markham collieries, is now long-demolished. NICK PIGOTT

ABOVE: A final look at the recently closed Dawes Lane works, with a coke push viewed from beneath the quenching tower.

brought up alongside and unscrews the oven's front door remotely. The same procedure is carried out at the rear door by the pusher machine, which then uses a powerful mechanical ram to push the red-hot coke through the guide car's cage and into the waiting coke wagon, resulting in a 'firework' display like no other!

The still-incandescent product is then quickly taken by the coke car to the adjacent quenching tower for cooling. That too creates a dramatic spectacle and at Port Talbot in 1981, a new set of ovens had to be built at Morfa to replace those at nearby Margam following

residents' complaints about clouds of smoke and plumes of steam. Today, the process is far more environmentally friendly, although the billowing of vapours as coke at 1,000 degrees hits cold air followed by water at a mere 10 degrees still qualifies as one of the most awe-inspiring sights in industry.

Not surprisingly, the operators and maintenance staff who work on the plant now have to wear special clothing and 'spacemen'-style helmets to protect them from the intense heat.

Renewable energy and sustainability are the bywords these days and in addition to the by-product capture, the

coal gas released during the coking process is recycled back to heat the ovens, making them largely self-sufficient in energy terms.

At the start of 2016, Tata Steel UK was planning to build a new benzole by-product plant at Appleby in conjunction with the rationalisation and was intending to keep that and the Morfa plant in operation, thus keeping alive one of Britain's great industrial traditions. But the company's decision in March to divest itself of all its UK interests had left the situation extremely uncertain as we closed for press. ●

BELOW: A panoramic view of Smithywood coking works in March 1982, which at the time was one of the last industrial premises in Britain still using steam locomotives on a regular basis. This huge plant, on the northern outskirts of Sheffield, was opened in 1929 and at its peak produced 6,000 tons of coke, 68,000 gallons of tar, 29,000 gallons of benzole and 100 tons of ammonium sulphate a week. It was demolished in 1987 and the site is now occupied by a business park. NICK PIGOTT

THE JEWEL IN
THE CROWN

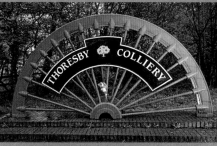

ABOVE: King Coal's golden crown. A close-up of the pulley wheels of the upcast shaft headstock at Thoresby Colliery, showing the crown that adorned the East Midlands' most productive pit for the last few years of its life. Note the jewel in the crown.
INSET RIGHT: An earlier form of crowning glory, photographed in June 1991 when the headgear still incorporated a frame hoist. BOTH: ROBIN STEWART-SMITH

THORESBY colliery was located just outside the village of Edwinstowe, in Nottinghamshire, and was established in the mid-1920s, producing its first coal in 1928.

It was said at the time to be one of the most modern coal mines in the world, but local landowner Lord Manvers, of Thoresby Hall, was not well disposed to the idea of a coal mine near his land and tried unsuccessfully to get it named Edwinstowe or Cockglode, after a local spinney.

Although upgraded in the 1950s, the mine was far more traditional than many of the more modern 'superpits' it outlived. The reasons for its longevity were partly related to the fact that it has benefited over the years from highly productive seams and was producing more than 1.5million tons a year - hence its proud reputation as 'the jewel in the crown' of the East Midlands coalfield. As can be seen from the illustration, its upcast shaft displayed a large golden crown, which was still proudly on display when the mine closed in July 2015.

The last seam to be worked there was known as the Deep Soft and there were originally three others - the Parkgate, High Hazel and Top Hard (or 'Barnsley'). Production at the final set of Deep Soft faces didn't start until 2010 and in its last month of operation, the colliery was operating around the clock, sending out at least three main line trainloads of power station coal a day and employing 379 men, some 300 of whom worked underground on a four-shift basis.

The mine's owner, UK Coal, wanted to keep it open and had even transferred locomotives and equipment from Warwickshire's closed Daw Mill Colliery, but with the subsequent collapse of world coal prices, the Government opted instead to provide a £10m grant for a 'managed closure'.

A few weeks before the pit closed, I was granted permission to take my final look at the underground workings of a fully operational colliery.

After a smooth and rapid cage ride down No. 1 shaft - which at 2,267ft deep is equivalent to more than

twice the height of London's Shard, Europe's tallest building - I stepped out into the strong breeze that characterised most deep workings. This was caused by the powerful ventilation fans, which circulated air around Thoresby's many roadways and galleries and sent it up the colliery's No. 2 shaft, which was also the one used for coal-winding.

The care-worn arched walls of the roadways looked as though time hadn't moved since they were built in the 1920s and there were 3ft gauge underground railways going off in every direction, serving storage areas, sidings, battery-charging stations and maintenance depots as well as the coal-getting districts.

The lines leading towards the coalfaces of modern mines were several miles long, which is one of the reasons why railways were necessary underground - to carry the miners to their place of work. For without the trains, they could spend as much as half their paid shift time walking to or from the coalface.

ABOVE: Although it no longer had an extensive internal-user rail system on the surface for the last few years, Thoresby retained its 3ft gauge tracks until mid-2015 for stabling purposes and to move wagons and locomotives into and out of the downcast shaft, seen on the right. NICK PIGOTT

ABOVE: A rare view inside an onsetter's cabin. These were located at the foot of the man-riding shafts and this one at Thoresby was 2,200ft below the ground. BARRY GRAHAM

They still had a long journey even after the train had dropped them off, having to walk almost a mile to the end of the coal-loading gate and then riding a conveyor belt to the face itself.

As faces were also usually at a deeper depth than the bottom of the shafts, the men at the cutting edge in some collieries had to toil at depths of 3,000ft or so… equivalent to England's highest mountain, Scafell Pike. Without trains and conveyors, they would have had to climb gradients as steep as 1-in-4 after a tiring shift in temperatures that could reach 100F (38C).

To reduce the risk of a coal dust explosion, Thoresby possessed a limestone spreader, used for applying white powdered stone dust all over the tracks, ballast and roadways in order to suppress the loose coal fragments and lower the fire risk.

Thoresby's coal was sent outbye via conveyors and taken to the surface in skip hoppers. Less than three weeks from closure, 48 skips were being wound every hour and the 20ft diameter winding wheels at the top of No. 2 shaft were spinning every couple of minutes, 22 hours a day, seven days a week.

Household coal (in medium-sized lumps) was collected from the pit by lorries after being processed in the coal preparation plant, but that intended for power stations was crushed and moved to the top of a large elevated bunker for dropping into main line railway wagons.

After closure, two of the colliery's

'Pony' locos were taken to the surface to be donated to nearby mining museums, one at Bilsthorpe and the other at Pleasley. The rest of the fleet were abandoned to their fate underground, along with its 15million tonnes of easily accessible reserves.

Thoresby's productivity rate remained high right until the end and the 700,000 tons it produced in the first half of 2015 were on target to give it yet another 1.5million tonne yield for the year. "We're more productive at the moment than we've ever been… but the country just doesn't want us," rued colliery manager Derek Main in the mine's final month. "The price of coal has fluctuated over the years and could easily rise again in the future – but by then it will be too late!" ●

BELOW: A general view of Thoresby Colliery a few months before closure. Note the difference between the concrete-clad upcast winding tower and the lattice steel downcast structure. At this particular pit, both sets of headgear featured substantial brick-built heapstead buildings at their bases. ROBIN STEWART-SMITH

THE BRAVE
NEW WORLD

YOUNGER readers and those who never saw a coal mine might be surprised to learn that many modern (and even not-so-modern) collieries were located in open countryside, surrounded by farmland.

Many modern mines had very few houses next to them, the NCB building large car parks adjacent to neatly trimmed lawns and laying on shuttle bus services for those miners who still relied on public transport.

Such mines also possessed structures that looked like concrete tower blocks instead of traditional winding wheels.

These were the so-called superpits. Some were built from scratch, others came about as a result of mergers between older or smaller mines, but they all had something in common – they were enormous.

One of the new state-of-the-art collieries – Comrie, in Fife – was built before the NCB came into existence. It was established between 1936 and 1939 by the Fife Coal Company, which sent its engineers to America and the European mainland to study all that was new in mining practice and then incorporated it into a showpiece

colliery in open countryside, complete with spacious layout – a complete contrast to the clutter and industrial grime of older pits and mining villages.

Underground, the roadways were generously proportioned and ventilation air was blown into the pit rather than being drawn through by extractor fans. At the face, each undercutter machine was so easy to operate and adjust that one man could do it. There were pithead showers and even a training school so that miners could better themselves by learning the history and theory of coal and its

strata. In many ways, Comrie set the seal for the NCB's own modernisation programme in the 1950s. Sadly, the pit never really lived up to its promise and although it lasted almost half a century, it was closed in 1986.

Another modern state-of-the-art Scottish colliery from the early NCB era - Rothes - also under-achieved due partly to drainage problems and was closed in 1962 after just four years of use. The political embarrassment this and other debacles caused resulted in abandonment of a partly built superpit at Airth, but another of the board's flagship superpits - Seafield, on the coast near Kirkcaldy - fared much better. That employed 2,500 men drawn from 13 old worked-out collieries further west, and had a coalface that was 100 yards long. It was described as being "more like an underground factory than a coal mine."

Other state-of-the-art mines in Scotland included Monktonhall and Bilston Glen, but by the time of the 1994/5 sell-off, there was only one complex left to privatise north of the border - Longannet/Castlebridge.

In England, superpits were opened at Parkside, near Manchester, in 1957, at Lea Hall near Stoke, in 1960 and in the Nottinghamshire coalfield - at places like Bevercotes and Cotgrave. In the eastern part of the Yorkshire field, Kellingley was opened in 1965 and in Staffordshire, there were major new or enlarged complexes such as Hem Heath and Wolstanton.

All-new mines in Wales were built at Abernant and Cynheidre, which were opened in the 1950s to exploit deep-lying anthracite seams at the western end of the South Wales coalfield, north of Swansea and Llanelli.

Superpits, most of which had large square or rectangular Koepe friction winding towers, were seen as the way forward in the brave new world of nationalised coal in the 1950s and early '60s, so it's rather ironic that two of the last three deep mines to survive in production until 2015 (Hatfield and Thoresby) had steel towers of the older design with traditional exposed winding wheels.

ABOVE: Block of flats? The difference between the Koepe winding towers of a superpit and those of a conventional mine were striking, as evidenced by this view of Parkside Colliery, near Manchester.

MERGERS: As seams became exhausted, it was not uncommon for neighbouring collieries to be merged underground with the surface buildings at one of them taken out of use or mothballed.

In such cases, one or more headstocks at the 'closed' site might well remain in operation for several months, or even years, for the use of men or materials or to facilitate ventilation. As each colliery thus had a different closure date, this can lead to confusion, so mining historians and researchers have to be particularly vigilant when recording such details. The surface buildings at Hucknall Top Pit, for example, closed in 1943 but its underground section continued to be worked for a further quarter of a century.

The subterranean linking of the Lancashire collieries of Mosley Common and Astley Green resulted in a complex that at one time was one of the largest in terms of workforce, with 5,000 men.

In the early 1960s, the NCB undertook a British Rail-style rationalisation programme that saw several smaller mines merged underground. In Leicestershire, Snibston, Whitwick and South Leicester were all linked up. ●

LEFT: A panoramic view of Rothes Colliery, Fife. Although many millions of pounds were spent by the NCB on the construction of this Scottish superpit in the 1950s, it never lived up to expectations and was closed in 1962 after fighting a losing battle with water inundation. Even before the end of main line steam in Scotland, its sidings had become overgrown and J38 No. 65901 is passing a rather forlorn scene in 1965. Still extant at that time was the aerial ropeway (lower right) leading to the spoil heap, while in the right background can be seen the tip of an older colliery near Coaltown of Balgonie.
W J V ANDERSON/RAIL ARCHIVE STEPHENSON

COAL AND STEAM:
THE PERFECT MARRIAGE

ABOVE: When this silhouette of Hudswell Clarke 0-6-0T No. S100 shunting the spoil tip at Yorkshire's Peckfield Colliery was taken in late 1969, the sun had set on main line steam just over a year previously, but the days of colliery steam were to last in a few places for more than a decade. GAVIN MORRISON

SOME collieries were tiny, wedged between a river and the side of a valley; others were enormous, sprawling across several acres of open countryside... but what almost all of them had in common was a railway connection.

Railways primarily came into existence to serve collieries, but as they developed into a nationwide network transporting general commodities and passengers too, they had the effect of opening up new coalfields and the mining industry thus found itself having to grow rapidly to cope with the new discoveries and increased demands.

The natural affinity between coal and trains didn't stop there, for the railway companies became big customers of the coal owners in order to fuel their steam locomotives – and for more than a century until the advent of reliable motor lorries, the coal owners needed the railways to get their product to every factory and into every little town and village in the land.

This was achieved by establishing a small coal yard or siding at virtually every country station, from where the local coal merchant would collect, bag and deliver with a horse and dray.

Today, such yards are a distant memory, although a few traditional merchants still do exist in 2016 and their storage areas – often separated by half-walls made of old wooden railway sleepers to denote different grades of coal – are a nostalgic reminder of a once-ubiquitous sight.

The first colliery branches were basic plateways and waggonways established in the 1700s to enable coal to be taken in chaldron waggons from pit to coastal or riverside wharfs. They would be allowed to run downhill by gravity, braked by a man riding on the vehicle and hauled back by horse when empty. On some lines, the process was speeded up by coupling a 'dandy cart' to the waggon, enabling the horse to ride in it on the way down.

The first successful railway in the world on which steam locos were regularly operated on a commercial basis was the Middleton Colliery line in Leeds, which opened in 1812 using a rack-and-pinion system.

ABOVE: Almost certainly the most unusual design of locomotive to work the surface lines of a major British colliery was the Beyer-Garratt 0-4-4-0T type, examples of which were based at Baddesley and Sneyd collieries in the West Midlands. This is maroon-liveried No. 3 operating at the latter pit in June 1961 and passing a delightful glassless signal that probably hadn't worked in years. COLOUR-RAIL

ABOVE: Before invention of the locomotive, chaldron waggons were run downhill by gravity.

ABOVE: Some of BR Western Region's Class 1500 pannier tanks saw use at Coventry Colliery after their main line days were over and received maroon paint in place of their BR livery. In this June 1969 scene, No. 1509 has its smokebox cleared of ash as classmate No. 1502 stands adjacent to the pit's winding tower. COLOUR-RAIL

RIGHT: The unusual sight of a large main line steam tender locomotive on a colliery internal system. Ex-LMS 8F 2-8-0 No. 48151 and an unidentified Class 58 diesel give shuttle rides at Sutton Colliery, Nottinghamshire, on September 10, 1988. ROBIN STEWART-SMITH

ABOVE: Ancient wooden-bodied wagons still in existence at Ashington Colliery in June 1987. NICK PIGOTT

RIGHT: Because they were introduced in the mid-1960s, Merry-go-Round coal wagons are associated very much with the diesel era, so a photo of one being hauled by a steam loco is an eye-opener. The location is Morpeth, Northumberland, and the newly built wagons are heading for Blyth staithes with a full load behind J27 0-6-0 No. 65842.

By the middle of the 19th century, the railway age was well established and virtually every major colliery was connected. Whenever a new mine was authorised in a hitherto-undeveloped area, the rail link normally had to be laid at an early stage in order to transport all the equipment needed to sink the shafts, erect the surface structures and build the colliery village. Sometimes the risk of constructing a single-track branch from the nearest main line would be borne by the coal company and sometimes by the railway company, although the latter tended to be cautious at that stage as the mine would not yet have proved a commercial success.

In the case of Bilsthorpe Colliery, the independent Mansfield Railway declined to build the necessary extension from the Rufford branch due to a dispute over rates, so the Midland Railway was appointed and

when it dragged its feet, the Great Central Railway was approached. That galvanised the MR, which said it would build a contractor's line at the Stanton Iron Company's expense but that, if the pit proved successful, the permanent line would be built at the MR's expense. The mine was indeed a success, although by the time the permanent way was required, the MR had become part of the London Midland & Scottish Railway, which duly picked up the bill.

By 1924, British mines were producing 267million tons a year and the railways were transporting 225m tons of that (84%). About 95m tons was exported and the railways' share of that pit-to-port traffic was an impressive 90%.

So keen was the Great Western Railway to guarantee itself a constant supply of good quality Welsh steam coal that it owned its own collieries at one time. The coal companies, on the

other hand, owned their own fleets of main line railway wagons, which, once unloaded at their destinations, had to be marshalled again in order to be sent back to their respective collieries. It was a colossal logistical operation, yet the wagons were never officially pooled despite such an arrangement being advocated several times in the 1930s.

At vesting day on January 1, 1947, just under a quarter of a million standard gauge wagons (60,000 of which were internal user vehicles) were handed over to the National Coal Board, which in turn handed them over to the British Transport Commission upon the formation of British Railways exactly a year later.

They were mostly wooden-bodied and almost invariably carried the name of the colliery or its owning company in large capital letters on the bodyside. Complicating the matter was the fact that many coal merchants and ▶

ABOVE: A spotless white overhead electric loco among the grime of a typical colliery scene – NCB No. 14 on the Harton Electric Railway in September 1968. The line linked Harton and Westoe collieries with the staithes in South Shields and didn't close until July 1989. TREVOR OWEN/COLOUR-RAIL

ABOVE: Former Mersey Railway 0-6-4T No. 5 *Cecil Raikes*, built in 1885 by Beyer Peacock, was purchased in 1904 for use on the Shipley Woodside mines system in Derbyshire and is seen with a rake of ex-LMS 40-ton bogie coal hoppers in the 1950s. RAIL ARCHIVE STEPHENSON

municipal utilities possessed their own wagons too.

As early as 1920 or so, the GWR was hiring 21-ton steel-bodied wagons to coal-owning companies to help eliminate old wooden wagons of eight to 10 tons capacity, and when BR came into existence in 1948, it decided to standardise on 21-ton and 16-ton wagons to replace the hotchpotch of private owner vehicles. Some 300,000 of the new types were built (the vast majority of them 16-tonners), but as an indication of how rapidly fashions change on the railways, even those had become

virtually extinct by the early 1990s. Fortunately, enough examples were preserved by the Great Central Railway to enable a coal train to be run and they can still be seen in operation on certain steam gala days and other special occasions.

The 21-tonners were 13 inches taller than their smaller cousins and not all colliery screen loaders could accommodate them, so they were usually allocated to specific routes.

In the mid-1950s, coal still accounted for 63% of all the freight carried by BR and South Yorkshire's Wath marshalling

yard (which wasn't even one of the largest on BR) was in 1954 taking in 53 full-length coal trains a day - an average of one every 28 minutes round the clock from no fewer than 21 different local collieries.

By 1958, BR's 16,000 steam locomotives consumed 10,745,000 tons of coal a year, but within a decade that figure would plunge to zero!

During the Beeching era of BR locomotive withdrawals and train service closures in the 1960s, the network of small coal yards (by then considered to be loss-making) was replaced by a smaller number of concentration yards, from where lorries could collect and deliver locally. The road transport companies, of course, soon realised that it would be cheaper and less hassle not to have the transhipment stage... and another form of traffic was lost to the railway.

From 1965, the Merry-go-Round (MGR) system of power station coal transport was introduced and in the last couple of decades, the four-wheeled wagons used on those MGR services have been phased out in favour of 100-tonne, 75mph bogie vehicles.

The last trainload of coal to depart from a British deep mine was the MGR service hauled from Kellingley to Drax by DBS No. 66152 on December 18, 2015 (followed by stockpile moves the following week - see page 122). Since then, all UK rail movements have been of imported or opencast coal.

Transport on the main line network was only part of the British coal story though. Virtually every colliery had its own internal railway system on the surface (in addition to the self-contained subterranean systems, which are dealt with in a separate chapter on page 109).

Standard gauge surface tracks were normally laid in and around the colliery yard to enable full and empty wagons to be moved in and out of washery screen sidings and be taken to the main line exchange sidings. As the years went by, these internal systems grew larger and more complicated and some even resembled minor marshalling yards with their own engine sheds, wagon repair depots and workshops. Some serving several collieries, such as the Lambton, Hetton & Joicey Railway, in County Durham, were extensive enough to be thought of as networks rather than branches.

The internal systems and their locomotives became part of the NCB in 1947, which partly explains why steam traction consequently clung on at collieries considerably longer than was the case on BR, well into the 1970s and even early '80s in some cases. The fact that the fuel supply for the engines was free and readily available also had a bearing!

Unlike BR, which implemented a standardised numbering system for the myriad locos it inherited, the NCB left such matters up to its area

Diversion of the East Coast Main Line at **Selby**

ONE of the strangest developments concerning the relationship between coal and main line railways involved the newly discovered coalfield in the district of Selby, North Yorkshire. In April 1976, the Secretary of State for the Environment, Anthony Crosland, ruled that the East Coast Main Line could be retained on its traditional route through Selby "only by leaving an unacceptable amount of coal incompatible with the new coal mining project".

The dramatic decision was thus taken to construct a major diversion several miles to the west in order to let the National Coal Board have unfettered access to the extensive coal deposits.

Selby continued to be served by trains, but lost its direct connection to York and its through main line expresses to London.

ABOVE: Seafield Colliery, just south of Kirkcaldy in Fife, was a modern superpit built by the NCB in the late-1950s alongside the Edinburgh-Dundee main line, along which preserved A4 Pacific No. 60009 *Union of South Africa* is passing with a steam special on September 8, 1973. The colliery was closed in 1988 and is now a housing estate. GAVIN MORRISON

managements. Some introduced systems revealing the division, area and colliery the machine was allocated to, others merely carried on with vague local arrangements.

Due to the fact that high-speed operation was most certainly not necessary on the switchback nature of most colliery tracks, quite a few former main line locos found a new lease of life on coal work after being pensioned off their primary duties. Among the best-known of these were former Great Western Railway pannier tanks but there were also ex-North Staffordshire Railway 0-6-2 tanks that ran in that railway's livery on the Walkden coal system and even an ex-London, Brighton & South Coast Railway E1 class 0-6-0T at Cannock Wood, in the West Midlands.

The hand-me-down nature of the arrangement continued into the modern traction era with many of BR's short-lived diesel shunters going on to have longer lives in industrial use than they did in BR service.

By far the most common form of steam loco used in UK collieries, however, were the 0-4-0 and 0-6-0 saddle tank types, thousands of which were in use at one time. When it came to the engine chosen to represent the NCB in the Stockton & Darlington Railway 150th anniversary celebrations at Shildon in 1975, Bagnall No. 2779, from not-too-distant Vane Tempest Colliery, was given the honour and proudly took its part in the cavalcade of glamorous and famous passenger locomotives. At the 'Rocket 150' celebrations five years later, the NCB was afforded an even greater honour, however – its Bold Colliery, in Lancashire, being chosen as the base for an all-star locomotive cavalcade with some spectators getting a grand view from atop the pit's spoil heap!

Among the most unusual engines to work in colliery service were two Beyer-Garratt articulated steam locos – No. 6729 at Sneyd Colliery, Staffordshire, and No. 6841 at Warwickshire's Baddesley Colliery, the latter loco now preserved.

ABOVE: British Rail Type 1s Nos. 20135 and 20071 slowly bring a rake of MGR wagons through the loading bunker at Bickershaw Colliery before setting off for Fiddlers Ferry power station on July 31, 1970. STEVE TURNER/RAIL PHOTOPRINTS

ABOVE LEFT: A little-known aspect of railway and mining history is the workmen's passenger train, known affectionately as the 'Paddy'. These were run by companies to take workers to remote locations they would have struggled to reach by public transport and utilised old coaching stock that had usually seen better days elsewhere. In this 1964 scene near Ashington, NCB 0-6-0T No. 31 is making good progress with former suburban coaches also lettered NCB. These miners were lucky, though… others, such as those who worked at Blaenserchan Colliery in South Wales, had to travel in converted goods vans! W J V ANDERSON/RAIL ARCHIVE STEPHENSON

ABOVE RIGHT: Also rare was a colliery with a passenger platform within its infrastructure. BR Western Region pannier tank No. 3647 waits at Glyncorrwg South Pit halt with an unadvertised workmen's service in April 1964. This 'Paddy' service ended later that year. A P GOFF

Main line connections for collieries were sometimes close by but sometimes several miles along a purpose-built branch, along which the industrial engine would trundle several times a day with loaded wagons, returning with the empties. (In steam days and before the advent of MGR, main line locomotives rarely worked on to colliery premises – but did so on a permanent basis in the later main line diesel era.)

The last standard gauge loco in regular internal use at a British deep coal mine complex was Barclay 0-6-0 diesel-hydraulic No. 615 of 1977, which worked at Gascoigne Wood disposal point in South Milford, Yorkshire, until at least 2004.

In addition to a standard gauge surface system, many mines in pre-skip winding days also possessed narrow gauge tracks of the same gauge as ▶

ABOVE: A view that epitomises the South Wales railway scene of the 1970s. The location is Aberbeeg Junction and British Rail Type 3 No. 37225 is bringing a train of 41 loaded coal wagons round the curve from Marine Colliery on April 25, 1976. R D YALLOP/COLOUR-RAIL

ABOVE: National Coal Board East Fife Area 0-6-0ST No. 7 propels a 16-ton wagon at Methil Colliery, Fife, in April 1962 while a classmate shunts a longer rake in the background.
W J V ANDERSON/RAIL ARCHIVE STEPHENSON

ABOVE: North Stafford Railway 0-6-2T No.2 was another former main line loco that ended up on coal mine duties, although Walkden Colliery ran it in its former NSR maroon livery.
RAIL ARCHIVE STEPHENSON

installed underground. This was to enable full tubs of coal to be moved from the shaft top to the weighhouse and washery and back again when empty. Such tracks were also used for storing wagonloads of spares and supplies before they were taken below for onward movement to the coalface or wherever.

In more recent years, the standard gauge industrial locos and wagons tended to be replaced by covered

conveyors on the surface and the many colliery sidings were consequently replaced by a much simpler layout enabling slow-speed Merry-go-Round trains to run into a rapid loading

bunker and then out again, either via a run-round headshunt or – where the space allowed – a balloon loop.

Conveyors underground also made the coal-carrying duties of subterranean narrow gauge systems redundant, although many were retained for man-riding purposes. ●

RIGHT: Hatfield Colliery, near Doncaster, closed in 2015 but its headstocks have been saved following an 11th hour intervention. In this July 2008 scene, an EWS (English Welsh & Scottish Railway) train headed by No. 66173 passes the colliery loaded – ironically – with imported coal from Immingham docks to Ferrybridge power station. JOHN CHALCRAFT

THE 'PADDY TRAINS'

ABOVE AND LEFT: An idea of the rough treatment mines locomotives received underground can be gained from these views of a Clayton-built Co-Co battery-electric loco when brand new in 2010 and after just 50 months in service at Thoresby Colliery.

A HUGE range of materials had to be transported underground in a modern colliery in addition to miners and coal. Firstly, there was the infrastructure required to develop the roadways, such as roof supports, then the equipment required to win the coal, especially machinery and conveyors, then the pipes and cables to provide electricity, compressed air, fresh air and water. Also needed were vehicles for emergencies - an ambulance car, a stretcher car and in some mines a fire-fighting wagon.

Back in the 1600s, four-wheeled tubs running on wooden rails had begun to replace sleds and barrows for the movement of coal underground, although at some locations tubs continued to be hauled by humans or ponies into the 1800s and even into the early 20th century.

Mechanisation began with the invention of reliable stationary steam engines in the 1700s. At first, those were placed underground (with their exhaust taken to the surface by flues in the shaft) and they hauled the tubs along the roadways using ropes, but so many fires were caused by that method that the boilers were placed on the surface and steam pipes were run down the shaft to underground cylinders. The problem with that was excessive condensation in the long pipes and although steam locomotives were invented in the early 1800s, it was not possible to use them underground for various reasons, the most obvious being ventilation and the risk of methane gas explosions.

That led to a search for more suitable sources of power and in the mid-1800s the first compressed-air rope haulage engines were introduced. Those were powered either by gravity or by stationary steam engines on the

surface, from which the ropes went down the shaft - still a complicated and unsatisfactory process.

After 1900, electrical equipment began to be used underground, but unless the mine could be proved gas-free, the electricity had to be generated by small power stations built at individual colliery pitheads and the need to flame-proof the subterranean equipment made the process slow to develop.

In those days, most coal was being hauled from the face to the pit bottom along narrow gauge tracks in tubs hauled by horses or ponies, of which there were an estimated 70,000 in British mines in the peak year of 1913.

In the 1920s, progressive colliery owners began to introduce small battery-electric locomotives (initially imported

from the USA) and at the end of that decade, British company Greenwood & Batley Co, of Leeds, also started building battery-electric locos.

The technology was in its infancy though - the battery power was relatively weak and the locos could not work for long between charges. It took the development of reliable diesel traction to mark a big breakthrough, but although a few diesels were tried underground in the late-1930s, they suffered from the same problem as steam engines - risk of fire and noxious fumes emitted in a confined space.

Pits with low to zero firedamp risk would at that time have been officially classified for fire risk purposes as Naked Light Mines, with the others being known as Safety Lamp Mines, but shortly after coming into existence, the NCB decided that the differentiation created too much of a 'grey area' and did away with the naked light classification. Thereafter, ▶

Test Tracks

BECAUSE it was not practical to test locomotives and drivers in underground conditions, test tracks were set up on the surface at selected collieries around the country. It was the NCB's aim to have a training centre in each of its area zones, not only to teach young apprentices but also to give refresher training to longer-serving miners to improve their knowledge and keep them up to date with advancing technology.

The centres were necessary to teach drivers how to handle the variety of hazards they might encounter underground, not the least of which was the control of skidding on adhesion gradients as steep as 1-in-15. To bring more realism to the tests, grease was often smeared on the rails. Some centres also featured short lengths of arched roadways built on the surface.

Once the coal mining industry began to contract after 1985, central training centres for each area became uneconomic and in the 1990s training was devolved back to individual pits ahead of the sell-off of mines to the private sector. Kellingley test centre was one of the last to survive, not closing until the early 1990s.

ABOVE: A 'streamlined' man-riding train on trial at Bevercotes Colliery test track in the 1980s.

ABOVE: Before the widespread introduction of battery-electric locos, diesel traction – suitably flame-proofed – was used underground at many collieries. This Huwood/Hudswell Clarke-built machine is hauling a six-coach man-riding train half a mile below the ground at Thoresby in March 1959.

all mines were assumed to be 'gassy' and all underground machinery had to be flame-proofed unless special exemptions had been granted.

To achieve this, electrical plant and traction motors had to be encased within one-inch-thick steel housings with machined faces and seals no greater than 20 thousands of an inch to prevent the possibility of a spark passing to the atmosphere. Part of the equipment's daily examination – which had to be done only by authorised electricians using special tools – ensured that no tolerances had slackened off during the previous day's running.

Even then, locos and other electrical apparatus had to be stopped and switched off by law if the methane content in the air rose higher than 1.25% and, as coal in its natural uncut state constantly emits methane, regular checks of firedamp-detecting equipment had to be made.

In addition to flame traps, diesel locomotives working underground had to have exhaust conditioners to remove noxious gases. These comprised an aluminium box in which there was a small quantity of water to extinguish any red-hot carbon soot before it could be emitted.

Each new design had to be submitted to the Safety in Mines establishment at Buxton, Derbyshire, for thorough testing followed by the issuing of what became known as a 'Buxton Certificate'. It was to be 1938 before the first such certificates were issued for diesel locomotives, but due to the war, their widespread introduction was delayed until the late 1940s. Once the NCB began its modernisation programme, huge loco fleets were introduced and by 1975, there were more than 1,000 locos under ground in Britain. With some coalfaces several miles from the pithead, however, their slow speed, especially on steep

gradients, meant that miners at some locations were spending as much as half their paid shift time travelling to and from work!

Pantograph-fitted electric locos (also known as trolley locos) drawing power off overhead wires were introduced in a few low-risk collieries, then, in the late 1970s, the Clayton Equipment Co, of Hatton, Derbyshire, perfected its 'Pony' battery-electric flameproof loco with rubber tyres, capable of climbing gradients as steep as 1-in-10 at reasonable speeds and small enough to go where the original ponies had trodden. As the company continued to improve the design, such locos were adopted on a large scale by the National Coal Board.

Clayton later produced much larger and more powerful Co-Co rubber-tyred locos, but they were restricted to haulage of men and materials as conveyor belts powered by flame-proofed electric motors continued to be preferred for the movement of coal. They could be operated continuously round the clock and were more suited to the automated nature of modern coal-shearing and loading machinery.

Locomotives nevertheless continued to be used extensively until the end of 2015 in the UK for transporting miners and materials.

Miners' passenger carriages have traditionally been nicknamed 'Paddy' trains or 'Paddy Mails' and the platforms as 'Paddy Stations'. These terms were throwbacks to the early days of main line railway construction in the mid-1800s when contractors' trains were run for navvies, most of whom were of Irish origin. Once the main lines had been built, the phrase largely fell out of use and was restricted to workmen's specials, but when underground man-riding trains began to be introduced on a widespread scale from the 1940s

onwards, it became a quasi-official part of mining terminology and remained in use until the very end of the deep-mining industry.

The quality and comfort of the man-riding carriages varied from colliery to colliery (some were enclosed by a roof, others not) and speed was usually restricted to about 5mph due to the twisting, undulating nature of the track in most mines – a result of subsidence and natural strata movement over the years.

Trains were referred to as running either 'inbye' or 'outbye', with 'inbye' being in the direction of the coalface. Each train crew consisted of a guard/shunter as well as a driver and some mine railways had basic colour-light signalling systems as well.

Each colliery possessed an underground locomotive maintenance depot – known in mining terminology as a garage – and battery-charging stations were positioned at various points around mines equipped with such motive power.

The NCB also modernised the entire underground rail vehicle fleet. Having inherited a mishmash of half-ton tubs with numerous different wheel sizes, it introduced thousands of large mine cars capable of carrying between two and four tons and fitted with brakes, springs and standardised couplings.

Many pits featured ferocious underground inclines, so several extra

Not what it **seems!**

Because most large locomotives were too long to fit inside a shaft cage and too complicated to take apart and reassemble underground, an ingenious way to take them down was devised. This involved 'hanging' them from the underneath of the cage, as seen in this remarkable shot at Silverwood Colliery, and then carefully bringing them round to the horizontal once they'd reached the bottom of the shaft. At some collieries, a specially designed metal sling was built in which to lower the locos.

safety devices had to be installed to prevent runaway trains in addition to the normal scotches and securing chains. These included gravel drags, hinged flip-over rail stops and hydraulically operated metal gates across the track.

The first major accident involving the use of locomotives underground occurred at Silverwood in 1966 (see page 95).

It was not possible for conventional steel-wheeled locos to haul trains up gradients much steeper than 1-in-15. Rubber-tyred locos were limited to about 1-in-10 and conveyor belts could not be elevated at more than 1-in-4 due to coal rolling back, so for anything steeper than that, a rope haulage system was necessary.

There were several different systems but basically they were either of the simple direct rope type, in which tubs were raised or lowered along an inclined track when required, or the endless-belt type, which operated continuously with tubs being clipped on and off the rope at each end. Some pits had subterranean rope inclines as steep as 1-in-2, alongside which refuges had to be provided every 20 yards in case of runaway tubs.

At Babbington Colliery, near Nottingham, miners went to work in ski lift-style chairs slung beneath a monorail, while Silverwood Colliery, South Yorkshire, had a very unusual rope-hauled high-speed 'Paddy Mail' in 1989, capable of hauling 124 men at 20mph. Worsley pit, near Manchester, sent its coal out by a network of underground canals built by the Duke of Bridgewater.

Another disadvantage of conveyors in the early years was that they could not turn corners, necessitating transfer points between sets of belts. Some collieries therefore used locomotives to move mine cars to the pit bottom. There, the loaded cars were pushed into the shaft cages either by hand or by special mechanical rams in the tracks. As they went in, they pushed an empty car out the other side, the empties having just descended in the cage from the pit top.

The empty cars would then be 'caught' by a creeper mechanism in the track which slowly pushed them into a line ready to be taken inbye by a locomotive.

Meanwhile, the full cars were wound up the upcast shaft, pushed out of the cage by empty cars on a similar principle and allowed to run down a slight slope before being slowed by a retarder for entry into the weigh house. After being weighed, they would be moved to tipplers, into which they were either pushed by hand or by another set of rams. The coal was then tippled out on to conveyors that took it to the preparation plant for washing and grading.

As part of the NCB's modernisation programme, the system described above was gradually updated so that conveyors replaced cars and the upcast shaft of each major colliery was fitted with a high-capacity coal-carrying skip in place of a cage. This eliminated the need for tubs or mine cars to be wound to the surface themselves.

By 1956, almost 2,000 miles of belts had been installed in roadways and surfaces of British mines by the NCB. By 1980, more than 95% of the coal moved underground was by those means – and in some collieries whose faces were many miles from the pit-bottom, men were allowed to ride on conveyors under strict safety conditions. It took quite a bit of practice to do this and whenever VIPs and other guests visited a mine, the belt would normally be stopped or slowed to allow them to climb on and off in safety.

At one time, locos and rail vehicles from closed collieries would be salvaged for spares or scrap, but with little prospect of re-use in recent years, the cost of bringing them to the surface has outweighed the value, meaning that that there are hundreds of locomotives, vehicles and conveyor systems abandoned deep in the bowels of the earth, many under water or gradually being crushed – a fact very few people outside the mining industry are aware of. ●

Overhead electric trains **under ground**

RAILWAYS powered by overhead electric wires are normally associated with main lines and urban tramways, but a small number of British collieries with low methane levels had underground railways powered by such a system.

The high risk of a spark between the pantograph and the overhead wire made catenary installation impossible in most pits but there were about half a dozen low-risk collieries in which the Mines Inspectorate granted exceptions to the regulations... but even then only in the intake airway roads, not the return airways.

The collieries concerned were Chislet (Kent), Gedling (Notts), Sandhole (Manchester), Silverwood (South Yorks) and Easington (Co. Durham). There had also been a system at Barnsley's Wharncliffe Silkstone Colliery as early as 1890 using a Yorkshire Engine Company-built overhead wire loco hauling coal wagons up a 500-yard long drift, but that operation is not thought to have lasted long.

The term used to describe overhead electric traction in the British mining industry was 'trolley locos' but they weren't actually fitted with trolley poles. Main line-style pantographs were preferred to give the overhead conductor wire more surface area over which to slide and thus reduce the sparking potential. The conductor wires also had to be fixed to spring tensioning devices to compensate for movement of the surrounding earth.

Metropolitan-Vickers pioneered the 20th century underground use of overhead electrics in the UK, with four locos being delivered to Sandhole Colliery in 1953. That system was highly successful and remained in use until closure of the mine in 1962, permitting large tonnages to be moved on a very narrow track gauge of 1ft 9in.

The overhead conductor system installed at Chislet in the early 1960s was the first of its type in Britain to work underground at 550V DC. It was 1²/₃ miles long and was used for man-riding trains as well as coal. The average gradient was 1-in-40 against the load but the English Electric-built locos – which replaced battery-electrics – were able to maintain a speed of 10mph.

Gedling Colliery's modernised system was introduced in 1983 to run on rails along a so-called underground 'motorway' (i.e. a high, exceptionally wide, well-lit haulage roadway). Upon closure of Gedling in 1992, the locos were transferred to Harworth Colliery but a planned underground electric line there never went ahead and they were returned to their Derbyshire-based manufacturer Clayton.

A fleet of overhead electrics that did see further use was Silverwood's, which were transferred to Easington Colliery following modifications.

In addition to the collieries mentioned above, at least two mines had overhead catenary on their surface rail systems. Those were Harton, which remained in operation until 1989, and Whittonstall, a 2ft 2in gauge system on the Durham/Northumberland border that served a number of drift mines in the area. It was a 500V overhead system and among its locos was a steeple-cab 0-4-4-0 built by Hanomag in Germany in 1910 and scrapped 20 years later.

ABOVE: How the twin-pantograph electric locomotives on the Gedling Colliery system looked.

PRIDE and PASSION

ABOVE: Cheers! There was nothing more satisfying after a long hard shift on the coalface than to slake the thirst with a pint on the way home.

LEISURE time was at a premium until the advent of the eight-hour working day in 1870, but the fact that many miners' families lived in close-knit areas in which virtually everyone shared the same occupation made a hobby or other interest vital if men were to be mentally stimulated.

Among the most popular pastimes were brass bands (many collieries had their own) along with bowls, pigeon-keeping, dog-racing and, of course football and rugby. Many mineworkers also kept allotments and specialised in growing prize vegetables despite the propensity for coal dust to get everywhere, even between the leaves of cabbages.

In the mid-1800s, some mining communities were more like Wild West frontier towns with rough navvies brought in from outside areas spending most of their wages in ale houses. Nevertheless, most Britons in Victorian society were God-fearing even if many mineworkers themselves weren't always so, and there was hardly a mining community in the country that didn't possess a church, chapel or other place of worship. This was particularly so in Wales, which in the 1860s had more than 3,000 nonconformist chapels, the most popular in the south being Baptist and Methodist chapels, which enabled miners to follow a religion other than the mainly Anglican creed of the coal owners.

In very tight-knit or isolated communities, miners and their families almost invariably turned out for the funeral of a colleague or village resident who had perished in a pit accident, even if they hadn't been particularly close to him personally. It was a sort of unwritten law and helped cement the bonds of pit community loyalty.

The church, chapel and clergy were towers of strength to miners and their families, especially in times of worry, hardship or tragedy. Many colliery workers consequently became lay readers or Sunday School teachers in their spare time.

Nobody needed to lock their doors in such communities in the 'black and white' days before mass car ownership. Monday was always wash day in the coalfields and wives would pray that the wind wasn't blowing from the smokestacks or washery screens. When a colliery closed, the wives and mothers living nearby would joke sarcastically: "Well, at least we can now buy white sheets for the beds!"

A woman's lot was made tougher if the men in her household were on different shifts, for that meant different sleep times, different meal times and (in the days before pithead showers) different bath times.

A widow with sons was something of a 'catch' due to the ability of males to bring more income into a household than girls and it was not uncommon for a newly widowed woman to be showered with proposals of marriage even before she had had time to bury her husband. It is reported that one woman with four sons accepted a proposal on her way to the funeral.

Although some pits were located in urban areas, the railways and factories of the Industrial Revolution created more jobs in formerly rural areas than agriculture ever could. This helps explain the enormous increase in population that took place in Britain during that era – some hamlets of 30 souls mushrooming into towns of perhaps 20,000 inhabitants in just a few years. As an example, the 1870s saw no fewer than 14 new collieries established within a two-mile radius of Hamilton West railway station in Lanarkshire.

In the early years of the 20th century particularly, a large number of collieries were established among open fields away from traditional mining areas

Glamour in the Coalfields

MINING areas weren't renowned for bright colours, so the communities positively encouraged their young ladies to enter 'Coal Queen' beauty pageants, which were often held in conjunction with annual miners' galas or picnics.

The contests really took off on an organised level when the National Coal Board was formed in 1947. The NCB and its successor, British Coal, co-operated enthusiastically with the National Union of Mineworkers in a pyramid of heats that ended with the coronation of the British National Coal Queen at either Blackpool or Skegness.

The prize for winning even a local heat could amount to more than a week's wages, so there were plenty of entrants and the winner enjoyed an interesting year performing opening ceremonies and suchlike at various pits in the area. She would also have a chance to go forward and have a crack at the national finals.

ABOVE: Jackie Barnard, Cadeby Colliery coal queen of 1982.

The Coal Queens of the 1960s, '70s and '80s were the wives and daughters of pitmen and even got to go down the mine now and again for promotional photos and suchlike. "I was petrified," said one winner. "I don't know how the men did it day after day."

Another commented: "There was none of the bitchiness you get at contests like Miss England. Everyone was friendly because we all came from mining families. I won a holiday to Israel, £1,500 and a gold watch."

The official UK Coal Queen contest began to die along with King Coal after the 1984/85 strike, but a few attempts at a revival have been made since.

Football... Keeping Famous Colliery Names Alive

THE collieries have gone but many of their old names survive thanks to their football and other sporting teams.

The most successful of these is arguably Frickley Colliery FC, long-term members of the Midland League in the years when that competition sat just below the Football League and who (as Frickley Athletic) finished runners-up in the national Football Conference in 1986. If that feat had been achieved today, the club would have been in the play-offs for promotion to the Football League.

A colliery side that once played at the country's most glamorous venue was Rainworth Miners' Welfare FC, which in 1982 reached the final of the FA Vase at the old Wembley Stadium.

In the North East, there have been many famous miners' welfare teams, including Chilton Colliery, which won the powerful Northern League in 1928, and Horden Colliery, winners of the North Eastern League in 1938.

Other non-league clubs bearing names reminiscent of their glorious past in the modern game include Gedling Miners' Welfare, Rossington Main and Ashington Colliers.

ABOVE: Kicking a football around in the streets of mining villages was how a lot of kids developed the skills that made them stars later in life.

and some of the more enlightened coal owners, inspired by the 'garden city' movement, provided pleasant tree-lined villages for workers and their families to live in. The Dukeries coalfield in Nottinghamshire was one that particularly benefited from this when it was established in the 1920s, seeing model villages created to serve such collieries as Blidworth and Bilsthorpe.

As these developed in virgin countryside with few, if any, existing amenities, it was necessary for the coal owners to provide housing on a similar basis to the 'tied cottages' of the agricultural industry. Although trying to appear paternalistic, some companies would impose strict conditions on their workers in return for a cheap rent. If a miner or his wife owed money at the company-owned shop, for example, it would be deducted from his wages. Many felt they were living in a sort of commune and that they might as well have been paid in coupons instead of money.

If their face didn't fit, they could be thrown out of their home as well as their job, with little comeback.

Such a village was Bilsthorpe, Notts, built on moorland several miles from established communities of any size and owned by the Stanton Iron Company. Between 1921 and 1931, its population went from 134 to 1,972 and then rose to 3,000 during the 1930s.

Rents were on a weekly lease and that kept mineworkers' minds concentrated on obeying the company's rules, which included keeping gardens tidy, keeping noise down and not engaging in 'immoral behaviour'. There was even a company-employed 'pit bobby' to keep law and order and those who stepped out of line regularly could find themselves jobless and homeless. Even dogs were banned for a while, especially whippets, as their presence was thought by the owners to encourage betting.

On the plus side, residents of mining villages tended to benefit from electric street lighting several years earlier than those of neighbouring communities (the 1890s in the case of Newstead, Notts) because generators began to be installed at collieries in order to power

ABOVE: One of the most common sights in Britain until the end of the 1960s was the coalman and his lorry. These men – often as coal-begrimed as the miners themselves – would heave hundredweight sacks off the back of their lorry and run (or stagger) along the side passages of people's homes before emptying the contents into the coal shed.

newly acquired machinery. Several communities also benefited from comparative luxuries too; the cinema built by the owners of Bullcroft Colliery for its miners had 1,000 seats and was even bigger than the cinemas in nearby Doncaster town itself.

A national Miners Welfare Fund was set up in 1920, funded by a penny levied on every ton of coal plus contributions from miners. This helped build institutes, with games rooms, libraries, brass band facilities and colliery football teams (see panel).

The strength and physique of miners made them good sportsmen. It was said that if a football or cricket boss needed a new centre-forward or fast bowler, he had only to whistle down the nearest mine shaft!

Among famous sportsmen who have come from mining communities are the Charlton brothers, Bobby and Jackie, and the legendary England fast bowler Harold Larwood of 'bodyline' bowling fame.

Until the 1960s, miners' welfare organisations would usually run a once-

From Gibraltar to **Minorca!**

MOST collieries took their name from the town or village in which they were located, but quite a few have borne unusual titles over the years. Here are some of the more unusual or exotic ones:

Dean & Chapter, Hole-in-the-Wall, Calcutta, Gibraltar, Minorca, Palace, Diamond, True Blue, Clock Face, Cross Hands, Milking Bank, Shuttle Eye, Fanny, Bryan's Leap, Gentlemen Colliers, Ledston Luck and Welch Whittle.

a-year trip to the seaside for members and their families, with the main line excursion train often undertaking rare passenger mileage along a freight-only line serving the colliery. Among permanent facilities provided was a miners' holiday resort at Rhyl, North Wales, and a convalescent home near Skegness, on the Lincolnshire coast.

The arrival of the NCB on the scene saw a widespread extension of canteens and leisure facilities from the 1950s onwards (some pits, such as Rossington, even had their own gym). The board had taken over ownership of all colliery houses in 1947 and, 39 years later, began selling them to tenants who wanted to buy. After only five years, 32,000 had been sold.

By then, miners were receiving wages that better reflected the risks and hard work and as a result, most were able to afford cars and foreign holidays, but the spirit and solidarity of the pit villages remained strong even after the devastating 1980s strike.

Sadly, there is no longer a single British mining village that has at its heart the original reason for its existence - an operational coal mine. ●

Reading all about it

UNLIKE railways, collieries have never attracted a mass enthusiast following. Consequently there have been no glossy monthly magazines available through high street shops. The main periodicals have been business titles targeted at mining professionals, such as the *Colliery Guardian*, staff newspapers for the benefit of National Coal Board employees such as *Coal News*, or the National Union of Mineworkers' own newspaper, *The Miner*.

Coal News started life in May 1947, only a few months after nationalisation, and provided a link between management and mineworkers.

COAL, NOT DOLE

CLASHES with authority seem to have been a tradition in the coal industry. As early as 1619, coal masters in Newcastle asked for injunctions against strikers and in 1740 'flying pickets' - a tactic that was to be used by Yorkshire miners in the long 1984/85 strike - first appeared when a withdrawal of labour closed most of the Tyne collieries and a big group from Newcastle travelled to a pit that had continued working in order to 'persuade' its men to join the dispute.

A United Association of Colliers was formed in 1825 followed by the first national organisation, the Miners' Association of Great Britain and Ireland, 16 years later. It soon attracted more than 100,000 members despite the fact that Ireland was better known for its peat and lignite deposits rather than coal, but the association was to prove short-lived. Several regional associations followed and eventually coagulated into the Miners' Federation of Great Britain (MFGB) in 1888, led by Arthur Cook, who famously declared during the dispute that was to lead to the 1926 General Strike: "Not a penny off the pay, not a minute on the day".

A miners' strike of 1893 was triggered by a drop in the price of coal that caused colliery owners to propose a 25% wage reduction in an attempt to maintain profits. That was rejected by the MFGB, which called for a national minimum wage. The result was a lock-out that went on for much of the summer.

The confrontation involved riots, violence and intimidation by gangs of strikers and ended in tragedy when troops were called in to quell a disturbance at Ackton Hall Colliery, near Featherstone. Faced with an angry crowd of 2,000 throwing stones and refusing to disperse despite being read the Riot Act, the soldiers were ordered to shoot and two miners were killed.

The dispute was finally settled by Government intervention and although the miners returned to work, they did not gain a national wage to replace the complex structure of locally agreed rates paid by the various mine-owning companies.

In 1910, an unrelated local dispute concerning a new seam in Penygraig, South Wales, led to miners there being locked out by the owners, Cambrian Combine. That escalated into a strike by all the workers employed by Cambrian, exacerbated by the company's plan to use strikebreakers. Police were called in and violent clashes ensued, culminating in rioting and shop window smashing in the Rhondda valley town of Tonypandy on the night of November

ABOVE: The longest and most bitter miners' strike took place in 1984/85 and was characterised by numerous physical clashes between police and pitmen. PRESS ASSOCIATION

8 that year. Home Secretary Winston Churchill decided to authorise the deployment of troops to reinforce the police contingent and although there are no records of shots being fired by the soldiers, the events made him unpopular in the South Wales mining communities even after he had become Britain's wartime leader 30 years later.

Meanwhile, pressure for a minimum wage continued and in 1912, Britain was gripped by its first national miners' strike involving every coalfield. Almost a million men took part and after a bitter dispute lasting more than a month (in which many had to scavenge for coal on spoil tips to keep their families warm), they finally managed to secure from the owners a Government-approved minimum wage and an agreement that colliers working in difficult seams wouldn't be disadvantaged.

Two years later, the First World War broke out and the mines were temporarily taken under State control. During the hostilities the Government approved several pay increases to ensure the collieries stayed in full production. Many miners hoped State ownership would become permanent after the war, but in 1919 the industry was handed back to its previous owners.

It wasn't long before another major dispute broke out, again resulting in a lock-out. This time it was caused by the Government's scrapping of wartime price controls in 1921, leaving the coal owners with lower profits, so once again they attempted to cut

miners' wages to compensate. That led to another national lock-out and strike, which lasted three months and severely damaged other coal-dependent industries and, with it, the country's economy. After three months, the miners were forced to accept terms that were substantially the same as those on offer when the strike started.

Such internecine struggles between different sections of the British community were proving almost ruinous in many respects, not only for the population as a whole, which had to stoically continue as best it could, but for the miners themselves. During the 1921 confrontation, for example, they were so desperate that they risked their lives by lowering themselves down abandoned bellpit shafts to salvage what pieces of coal they could find for their families.

Even when the lock-outs ended, there were so many miners looking for work (as many as 200 at each colliery in some cases) that the companies had to employ police to keep them away as they were hindering work at the pitheads. Many were still behind with their rent and other bills as a result of the 1921 stoppage when the even bigger 1926 dispute started.

By then, Churchill had become Chancellor of the Exchequer and had put the country on the Gold Standard, increasing the cost of exports by 10%. Britain's pits, already at a disadvantage against foreign producers following the First World War, could not compete with overseas mines and coal began

to stockpile at the pitheads. At first, the Government provided a subsidy to maintain wages at their present level but when the subsidy ran out in April 1926 there was yet another lock-out.

The Trades Union Congress called the infamous General Strike in support and the major industries of the entire country ground to a standstill in May of that year, but after nine days in which members of the public volunteered to keep the railways and other essential services running, the resolve of the TUC and the other unions collapsed and the miners were left to continue the fight on their own for six more months.

It all ended in ignominious defeat, for at the end of the dispute those fortunate enough to still have a job were forced to go back on longer hours and lower wages, making a mockery of Cook's rallying call. Many remained unemployed for several years.

At the height of the 1926 dispute, many miners affiliated to the MFGB in Nottinghamshire were unhappy with the way the federation was handling matters and this led to the formation of a moderate breakaway body, the Nottinghamshire & District Miners' Industrial Union, under the leadership of George Spencer. Although the so-called 'Spencerites' reluctantly decided in 1937 to return to the federation, the difference in attitude between the Nottinghamshire men and the more militant trade unionists in the rest of the industry (especially in neighbouring Yorkshire) was to cause long-lasting animosity that would have serious implications years later.

The wounded MFGB remained in existence until being reorganised into the National Union of Mineworkers (NUM) on January 1, 1945 – just two years before formation of the National Coal Board with which it was to cross swords so many times in later years.

Although it is a sweeping generalisation, it is worth noting that

ABOVE: Among the most powerful symbols of miners' solidarity over the years have been the banners of the individual union lodges and federations. Similar in style to those produced by the Soviet Union to inspire industrial and agricultural workers during the years of the revolution, they often portrayed an idealised world in which happy families would benefit from lifelong security.

NCB executives in the 1960s and '70s tended, on the whole, to view East Midlands miners as moderates and those from the other large coalfields as traditionally more militant. The Kentish miners fell into the latter category, partly because of a large influx of Northerners displaced by pit closures in their own areas.

Compared with what had gone before and what was to come, the Fifties and Sixties were relatively peaceful times in the coalfields. Although the natural reduction in collieries through closure of old and uneconomic pits had resulted in the huge but gradual loss of 400,000 jobs, the NUM had offered little resistance due to the high investment in the industry generally and its leaders were in any case reluctant to make

demands on a Labour Government during the mid-to-late Sixties. But the old order was changing and a tranche of younger activists with left-wing views were taking over positions on the NUM area councils.

Signs of what lay ahead came in October 1969 when calls for a better deal for surface workers escalated into a major unofficial strike affecting 140 of the nation's 307 collieries (including all those in Yorkshire). It was settled after two weeks but during that time, the NCB lost £15million and 2½million tons in lost production.

That 1969 strike was the first major dispute since the 1920s and the first since then to feature widespread picketing of mines by strikers.

Less than three years later, the 'flying pickets' were in action again, this time as part of an official dispute. The 1972 strike was staged over a pay claim and lasted for almost the whole of January and February, during which time the country briefly entered an official state of emergency. The dispute was characterised by violence at numerous pits and a picket was killed in an accident at Hatfield Colliery, near Doncaster, when a coal lorry mounted a pavement during clashes. In Birmingham, more than 2,000 pickets descended on Saltley coking plant in a bid to prevent supplies from entering and leaving.

The strike ended when the Conservative Government of Edward Heath acceded to the wage demands, but as the 1970s progressed, runaway inflation began to force up prices and erode the effect of pay rises. When the Government attempted to tackle the inflationary pressures by capping public sector pay, the NUM invoked an overtime ban.

That caused shortages in coal supplies and in December 1973, Heath announced that the country was to be put on a three-day week to conserve electricity consumption. For the next few weeks, power cuts were enforced on a regular basis and all but essential industries and services were prevented from working.

The NUM's response was a ballot leading to a full-blown strike, which began on February 5, 1974. Two days later, an angry and frustrated Heath called a snap general election on the issue of 'Who governs the country?'

He confidently expected the electorate to back him with a mandate to sort it out, but instead – seemingly tired of the constant strife and the Government's inability to deal with it – many floating voters switched sides and Heath failed to win a majority. After failing to gain Parliamentary support from minority parties, he conceded to the socialist Wilson administration, which acceded to the miners' demands. A second general election in October 1974 gave Wilson an overall majority.

ABOVE: In the long strikes of the late 19th and early 20th centuries, workless miners and their families often had no option but to scavenge spoil heaps for tiny lumps of coal that had slipped the net in the screens. This Lancashire scene was photographed in 1893.

Other **Unions**

IT is widely believed in non-mining areas that the whole of the coal industry was a traditional hotbed of discontent but that was not the case in all regions. In fact, the East Midlands areas of Nottinghamshire, Leicestershire and South Derbyshire had a moderate reputation that resulted in them falling out with their more militant brethren and forming the Union of Democratic Mineworkers (UDM) in 1985.

The East Midlands men felt that the NUM had tried to railroad them into industrial action for political reasons. They also objected to the picket line intimidation of non-strikers.

Other unions in NCB days were the National Association of Colliery Overmen, Deputies & Shotfirers (NACODS), which represented middle managers, and the Colliery Office Staff Association (COSA) for white-collar workers on the surface. Senior managers belonged to the independent British Association of Colliery Management.

The NUM is still in existence today and its headquarters is still in Barnsley, but it has a very small number of members and mainly concentrates on providing help and advice to former miners struggling with injuries and industrial diseases.

ABOVE: Commemorative plates issued by the NACODS union (left) and the UDM.

The 1970s were notorious in British industry generally for constant walk-outs and 'down-tools' incidents over numerous grievances, many of a local nature. Senior men found it extremely difficult to manage or plan businesses efficiently and there was massive anger and frustration in management and political circles at union activities. At one time, the NCB was described as an unmanageable business and it was clear that even Labour Government ministers were tearing their hair out with exasperation over the apparent hopelessness of the situation.

After the infamous 'Winter of Discontent', the electorate was so fed up that the Conservatives were restored to power in 1979 with a mandate to 'sort the unions out'. Their leader by then was the uncompromising Margaret Thatcher, a staunch right-winger who came to power pledging to curb inflation and reduce union power.

Rumours of a 'hit list' of 50 pits began circulating in 1980/81, prompting another wave of militancy in the coalfields and resulting in the Government being forced into a climbdown to avoid another damaging miners' strike. Prime Minister Thatcher shelved the pit closure programme on that occasion but her later memoirs revealed that she vowed to herself that no union would be allowed to wield such immense political power again. In 1983 she was re-elected with a huge majority and shortly afterwards replaced the long-serving and relatively moderate NCB chairman Sir Derek Ezra with the

uncompromising ex-head of the British Steel Corporation, Ian MacGregor.

A few months previously, the NUM had elected as its president a firebrand left-winger who had been involved in organising the 1970s strikes. His name was Arthur Scargill, an ex-Yorkshire miner and a former member of the Young Communist League.

The stage was set for a classic confrontation between the right and left wings of British politics**...**

The 1984/85 strike: In March 1984, the Government announced that the billion-pound annual subsidy to the coal industry would be withdrawn, that the energy market would be opened up to cheap imports and that loss-making collieries would be closed.

The reasons were threefold: Firstly, the Prime Minister was an advocate of free market policies; secondly, the coal industry was once again in decline following the temporary boost of the

mid-1970s and thirdly, the Conservatives had a long-term plan to privatise the industry and needed to streamline it in readiness.

The NUM, on the other hand, was convinced there was a fourth reason - 'payback' for the ignominious defeat the miners had effectively inflicted on the Heath administration 10 years earlier.

The miners faced a stark dilemma: accept a slow and painful death or man the barricades once more to try to save their jobs. The majority decided to back their new leader and opt for the latter.

Given the outcome of their successful 1970s campaigns, they were confident they could force the Government to capitulate again as it had in 1981, but this time there were three chinks in their armour. Firstly, the strike began in the spring, secondly the Government had ensured that coal stockpiles at power stations were at maximum level, and thirdly, the miners were no longer a united force, for the East Midlands men decided to carry on working in protest at the strike being called without a ballot of individual members, which they considered illegal and undemocratic.

The traditional solidarity of the striking miners - backed by loyal wives and families - ensured that the dispute dragged on for more than a year and the coalfields became battlefields as police and miners clashed in what almost degenerated into a class war.

The strike has been described by the BBC as 'the most bitter industrial dispute in British history'. Much of the bad feeling resulted from the Government's decision to draft in officers of the London-based Metropolitan Police - another case of history repeating itself, for members of the same force had been sent to help quell the South Wales riots in 1910.

A surprising amount of the violence was, however, internecine in nature... directed by strikers against strike-breakers (or 'scabs' as they were referred to). In some cases, it extended to attacks on property and death threats to the families of working miners. Over the year, tens of thousands of stones and half-bricks were hurled at the buses and other vehicles - some of them

ABOVE: The protagonists: NUM leader Arthur Scargill and NCB chief Ian MacGregor, who went head to head in the 1984-85 strike. **ABOVE RIGHT:** A rare photograph of Prime Minister Margaret Thatcher wearing a miner's helmet during an underground visit to Yorkshire's Wistow Colliery in 1980.

armoured – taking strike-breakers into and out of collieries.

There were pitched battles in the streets and gardens of pit villages as police charged the miners, hitting them with batons and riot shields. The miners fought back with stones, fists, boots and anything else they could lay their hands on.

At its height, 142,000 mineworkers were involved, making it the biggest dispute since the 1926 General Strike. Many police and pitmen were seriously injured in the clashes, but remarkably, fatalities were restricted to three – two pickets plus a taxi driver who had been driving a non-striker to work. Two miners were sentenced to jail for his manslaughter.

The strike broke families financially as well as morally. For the first few weeks, the households managed to get by. After a couple of months they had eaten into their life savings and before long they were having to borrow from relatives or sell belongings just to put food on the table. Disillusioned and desperate, many were forced to return to work and by February, there were more at work than on strike. Tragically, many families are still split to this day; there are brothers who haven't spoken to each other for 30 years because one went back to work and the other didn't. Some marriages even broke up because of the strain everyone had been under.

The dispute finally ended in early March 1985 – a defining moment in British history for it significantly weakened not only the NUM but also the entire trade union movement in the UK. The men who had held out to the bitter end went back to work with their heads held high, but the atmosphere in the collieries was never the same again and the strike remains a touchy and highly controversial subject.

Within weeks of it ending, the first of the new tranche of pit closures were implemented. It certainly looked as though the Government was determined to cut the industry and the NUM down to size.

Cortonwood was one of the first to go in 1985, followed by almost all the 70-odd pits MacGregor had always had on his hit list (despite his denials to the contrary the previous year). Most miners seemed resigned to taking the NCB's enhanced redundancy packages; there was no more fight left in them, only bitterness.

The decision of the railway unions to support the strike had enabled road hauliers to take advantage… and after the dispute they capitalised by negotiating many long-term contracts with the coal board to the detriment of the rail industry. Much of the traffic never did return to rail.

There is a school of thought that the Government might have orchestrated the strike in order to trigger a confrontation for which it had prepared well, but some reports claim

ABOVE: Barnsley's last mine: The headstock and winding house of the former Barnsley Main Colliery, preserved but daubed with graffiti.

ABOVE: The NUM's turreted headquarters building in Barnsley.

that the NUM was preparing to call a strike in early 1984 anyway. After all these years, the real truth will probably never be known. What is known, courtesy of 1978-dated documents released under the 30-Year Rule, is that plans had indeed started that year to be drawn up to curb the strength of the NUM.

Interestingly, the role of South Yorkshire Police in clashes at Orgreave coke works in 1984 hit the news again in May 2016 when alleged links were made between that dispute and the force's handling of the Hillsborough stadium tragedy of 1989.

Where the '84/85 strike will stand when history comes to judge the coal industry is a moot point. It all depends which side of the political fence it's viewed from. Those of an intractable right-wing persuasion will see it as an ill-advised campaign that ironically destroyed everything it had set out to save; those on the political left will

take the view that the miners did what anyone else would have done in their position… and that was to defend their jobs and their livelihoods. It is clear that if they had stood by and done nothing, the pits would eventually have closed anyway, so their view was that they had at least to make a fight of it.

In terms of losing a valuable national asset – not just the coal itself but the vast network of mines so painstakingly built up for the nation by previous generations – the successive Governments of the 1960s-2015 era can be said to have cut off their noses to spite their faces, but neutral observers will doubtless point to the 30 years of relatively strike-free harmony that followed the mid-Eighties in British industry generally.

It's just a tragedy that so much irreplaceable infrastructure and so many lives have had to be wrecked to achieve it. ●

GOING DOWN
AT AN ANGLE

THE principal difference between a deep mine and a large drift mine is the means of entry and exit. Once underground, the infrastructure and hazards are very similar.

The earliest drift mines were contemporaries of vertical bellpits and followed the seam, either on the level or at a slightly ascending inclination to make them self-draining.

Until the Second World War, drifts were basically used to exploit areas of shallow coal and most used rope haulage for transport, although conveyors began to be used later.

In the early NCB era, it was realised that many shallow shaft mines could be made more efficient if the coal-raising shaft was replaced by a surface drift and conveyor, thus allowing continuous production from face to surface rather than intermittent shaft winding. Many reconstructions were carried out; South Derbyshire's Cadley Hill Colliery, for example, was provided with two parallel drifts, one containing a high-capacity cable belt for the coal, the other a high-speed man-rider.

As conveyor technology improved, seams as deep as 700 yards could be accessed by drift mines.

At such reconstructed collieries, the drift was almost invariably used for coal-raising and at least one winding tower and shaft would be retained for handling men and materials.

West Yorkshire's Prince of Wales Colliery, originally sunk in 1872, had large new drifts inserted in the 1970s that were designed to more than double its production and extend its life expectancy to beyond 2000. Nottinghamshire's Bevercotes superpit was also provided with a surface drift from new in addition to a shaft access. Snibston had a drift, Daw Mill had two shafts and one drift – and the preserved Big Pit at Blaenafon had one of each type, the consequent lower headstock maintenance costs said to be one of the reasons why it was selected for preservation.

Working in a drift mine might not, at first glance, seem as bad as working in a deep mine, yet before the advent of proper health & safety regulations, men were so desperate for money that they would follow coal seams further into the sides of mountains than was good for them. By advancing the face further and further from the mine entrance, they would reach areas that had barely enough air to keep a candle burning and would have to keep coming out of the mine to allow their lungs to recover.

In July 2015, Britain's last major drift mine – at Aberpergwm, near Glynneath in South Wales – ceased operation and was put into care and maintenance by its North American owners Walter Energy. It was a bad time for collieries, for the closures of Hatfield and Thoresby deep mines were implemented at the same time. The reason for all three closures was the same – low coal prices exacerbated by new carbon taxes.

BELOW: The rugged beauty of the South Wales valleys is evident as an 'Austerity' 0-6-0 saddle tank drifts down from Graig Merthyr drift mine with a nine-wagon train in the summer of 1978. Note the conveyor taking the spoil upwards and thereby creating a new peak in the hills around Pontarddulais. GEOFF SILCOCK

Less than two years earlier, the Unity drift mine at Cwmgwrach had also been 'mothballed' with the loss of 180 jobs. Like nearby Aberpergwm, it worked some of the finest quality anthracite in the world and had reopened with room & pillar operation in 2008 only to go into administration in 2013. It had been planning to make an expensive change to longwall mining but required further funding to purchase longwall equipment.

Unity, which is said to have reserves of up to 90million tonnes of coal, was established on the site of the former Pentreclwydau drift mine, which closed in 1967. As this publication closed for press, there were hopes in the Neath Valley that both mines might eventually resume operations once trading conditions improve.

The traditional name for a small drift mine is footrail (pronounced footrill) and, remarkably, there are still a few very small ones left in existence, although not all work on a regular basis. These include Ayle Colliery, near Alston in Cumbria, Hilltop Colliery, in Lancashire, and a number in the Forest of Dean, Gloucestershire. Most operate on traditional means with dram tubs, rope haulage and wooden pit props. There used to be several hundred small private drift mines in South Wales too, but they were killed off by low coal prices. Even in the 1980s, they were receiving only £38 a ton for their coal from the Central Electricity Generating Board while nearby NCB pits were being paid £52 a ton.

In 2016, there is hope that a new drift mine can be established at Crofton, in West Yorkshire. The New Crofton Co-Op Colliery has put forward proposals to mine 200,000 tonnes of coal a year, creating 50 jobs and supplying to the power industry. If successful, the mine would be operated as a workers' co-operative.

On a light note, it is said that some of the young colliers working in drift mines in years gone by would deliberately let their lamps go out at about midday on a Saturday. This would mean having to walk back to the entrance to relight them, but once there, they would have less than an hour to the end of their shift, so they would sign off early… and hurry off to play or watch rugby! (In a shaft mine, they wouldn't have been able to do that as the onsetter, banksman and cage winder would all have to have been involved.) ●

Forest Free Miners

THERE is one type of coalmining in Britain that has been a law unto itself for centuries – Forest Free Mining.

The exact origins have been lost in the mists of time, but back in the 13th century, men who worked the tiny hillside pits and adits of Gloucestershire's Forest of Dean were asked by King Edward I to use their skills to tunnel through the fortified walls of Berwick-upon-Tweed during sieges to recapture the border town from the Scots. In return, they were granted privileges, one of which was the right for any male born within 'the Hundred of St Briavel's' to mine coal and iron ore for ever without paying dues or royalties.

In granting this right, the monarch stated that the custom had already existed informally 'since time out of mynde' and it has since been established that the coalfield had been worked as early as Roman times.

The rights, which also require each man to have worked in a Royal Forest of Dean mine for at least a year and a day, were ratified in the Dean Forest (Reforestation) Act of 1668 and reconfirmed by Parliament in 1838.

The tradition has since been handed down from generation to generation and been enshrined in law, so much so that when the British mining industry was nationalised in 1947, the men from the Royal Forest were exempted and allowed to continue owning their own areas of coal-bearing land (known locally as 'gales') along with the small drift mines they had established.

By that time, proper deep-mine collieries had also been established in the forest but those came under the licence of the National Coal Board upon nationalisation. The last to survive – Northern United Colliery at Cinderford – closed in 1965.

The gales remained exempted following the handing of Britain's coal reserves to the newly formed Coal Authority in the 1990s and the drift mines have continued to be worked by their tiny teams of perhaps just one or two men each, using timber roof props, picks and shovels in the traditional manner supplemented by a few hand-held pneumatic tools. The miners work seams (known as delfs) of about 2ft 6in thickness and to do so, often have to lie on their side or stomach.

In early 2016, about half a dozen gales – including Hopewell, Monument, Phoenix, Wallsend, Haywood and Reddings – were still functioning either full-time or part-time, their owners digging out small amounts of bituminous coal for local domestic sale on an occasional or as-required basis.

The current low price of coal has not deterred these one-man bands as the men take the view that they would rather be gainfully employed and at least making a modest living rather than sitting around idle. Hopewell supplements its income by allowing public museum tours in a worked-out part of its mine for an admission fee and is well worth a visit (see page 126).

It is feared that the free mining tradition will eventually die out due to the closure a few years ago of the maternity unit at Dilke hospital in Cinderford. Although there are ongoing moves for full rights to be extended to females, the closure has drastically reduced the number of people born within the qualifying area of the Hundred and means that only a baby born at home in the area would in future qualify.

ABOVE: One of the thin seams underground at Hopewell drift mine and (right) the entrance to the part of the mine that is still being used. NICK PIGOTT

TAKING THE
ROOF OFF!

ALTHOUGH sourcing of coal from outcrops in ancient times could loosely be classed as 'opencast' and there were small quarry-style pits in Staffordshire in the 1840s, the concept of surface mining as we know it today didn't really get under way until the early 1940s when the Second World War caused a sudden demand for extra coal with insufficient time to sink new shafts.

Until then, excavators and mechanical shovels had not grown large and powerful enough to strip off huge tonnages of overburden, but the advent of giant dragline machines enabled opencast mining – effectively quarrying – to become more viable.

The National Coal Board's Opencast Executive came into being in April 1952, its sites having previously been operated by contractors on behalf of the Ministry of Fuel & Power.

The main UK sites today are privately owned and are located in Northumberland, South Wales and central Scotland, with Shotton (north of Newcastle), Ffos-y-Fran (near Merthyr Tydfil) and Tower (near Hirwaun) being among the largest.

Banks Mining, Celtic Energy, Hargreaves, Miller Argent and UK Coal Surface Mines Ltd are companies active in the field and applications for pit extensions continue to be made even though a number of surface mines have closed in the last three or four years due partly to the low price of imported coal.

Many strip mines are on the sites of former collieries that were closed before their reserves had been fully exploited and in some cases, such as the former Minorca Colliery, near Measham in Leicestershire, so much coal has been extracted (1.9million tonnes) since 2013 that it is a wonder the original mine was ever closed in the first place! Minorca

closed as this publication was going to press in 2016 after finally exhausting all the coal it had been licensed to extract. The owners had permission to mine the site of the nearby Measham Colliery but decided against it on economic grounds.

Of course, it is much easier to identify and access coal seams once they are all exposed to the open air, but the big drawback with opencast is the sheer size of the scars made on the earth's surface. The erecting of overburden mounds or bunds around sites while they're being worked helps to screen them from public view and the majority of sites are restored to farmland or woodland afterwards.

The rock above and between most coal seams is predominantly shale, mudstone and sandstone and as that is removed, it is typically used to back-fill previously excavated areas. Then, when the coal has been removed, the topsoil and subsoil are placed back on top. Because rock naturally swells and expands during the excavation processes - a phenomenon known as bulkage - it is possible to restore the land to about the same level it was before the mining started.

Strict environmental regulations govern opencast mining, including a requirement to mitigate the risk of foul water polluting local watercourses and a restriction on the number of heavy lorries allowed to leave and enter sites that are not rail-connected. Noise and dust suppression measures are also enforced, but controversy continues to rage over such mining techniques.

Although the operations are classed as 'shallow', this is a relative term where coal mining is concerned, for in some locations, even the seams nearest the top can be well over 100 metres deep and this means that so-called 'surface mines' can extend as far into the earth as some of the deepest British stone quarries. To achieve such depths naturally requires a massive surface area to be stripped and one pit near Margam, South Wales, created a void about a mile and a quarter across, while another in Leicestershire engulfed an entire farm... including the house and barns, which literally vanished off the face of the earth as the mine expanded.

In theory, there is no limit to how deep an opencast mine could be excavated, but reaching the very deepest coal seams would require voids that could be the size of a small town and it thus becomes uneconomic beyond pre-determined weight ratios of overburden versus coal.

LEFT: A thick seam – more than 12ft in places – has been opened up in recent years on the site of Leicestershire's Minorca Colliery, which closed in 1980 before its reserves could be fully exploited. This photo, revealing the remarkably well-defined dividing line between the coal and the shale mudstone above it, was taken on February 16, 2016 with permission from UK Coal Surface Mining Ltd. Since then, the mine has closed and restoration of the land is taking place. NICK PIGOTT

ABOVE: Opencast coal mining Chinese-style! Three Class SY steam locomotives, all moving, come into line with each other momentarily as they make their way along different levels of the giant 'crater' at Jalainur, northern China, on March 9, 2009. (This remarkable three-way line-up actually occurred and is not the result of studio trickery). NICK PIGOTT

ABOVE: This cast iron-wheeled rail veteran had been abandoned when Minorca Colliery closed and was found during the opencast mining operation.

Apart from the method of extraction, surface mines are similar to traditional collieries insofar as they ideally need a means of washing and grading the coal before it is sold to power suppliers and other customers. For this, some have preparation and washing plants located at a nearby disposal point and distribution centre, to which the coal is taken from outlying pits. Among such installations are Onllwyn and Cwmbargoed, the latter producing Welsh steam dry cobbles, which are softer than anthracite but cleaner-burning than bituminous house coal.

The fact that some opencast mines expose the subterranean galleries of demolished collieries has given rise to a number of remarkable 'finds'. These include the discovery of old room & pillar workings, which give historians and industrial archaeologists a first-hand view of just how underground mining was undertaken in previous centuries. One such 'honeycomb', uncovered during strip mining at Coleorton, Leics, in the early 1990s, was reliably dated back to the late 1400s, making it one of the oldest in the world. The height of those medieval workings was an average 4ft 6in.

The Wellington/Coalbrookdale area of Shropshire was once riddled with more than 200 ancient and relatively shallow bellpit cavities. Opencast mining not only extracted 1¼million tons of coal that would otherwise have been left in the ground but made the land stable enough for developments connected with Telford New Town in the 1970s.

Also unearthed in various parts of the country in recent years have been items of mining equipment abandoned underground when collieries closed, such as coal-cutters, conveyor belts, locomotives and mine cars. An iron-wheeled flat wagon recently uncovered when the old Minorca Colliery was exposed is thought to date back to Victorian times.

Opencast accounts for 80% of coal production in Australia and almost 70% in the United States (which has the largest site in the world, at Powder River Basin). China too has some vast open pits several miles long, yet many British members of the public are surprised when they find that such mines still exist in the UK - and 'green' campaigners continue to protest whenever a new site is identified (the scenic Druridge Bay in Northumberland being the latest 'battle' front).

The stark truth of the matter, however, is that closure of the last British deep mine in 2015 and the mothballing of the country's two largest drift mines has made opencasting more important than ever. For without it, the country would be in the economically and politically insecure position of being 100% reliant on imports to fuel its coal-fired power stations.

Until the nation has fully developed a range of alternative ways of generating electricity, opencast mining is likely to continue. ●

ABOVE: A general view of the Minorca opencast site on February 16, 2016. Such operations are able to reach depths of several hundred feet but cannot access the higher-quality 2,000 and 3,000ft seams Britain has now abandoned with its decision to end deep mining. NICK PIGOTT

THE LAST ONE
KELLINGLEY

ABOVE: This view of Kellingley's two Koepe winding towers was taken with permission from the top of the adjacent coal preparation plant just a month before the colliery closed. NICK PIGOTT

THE honour of being the last of Britain's many deep mines to survive in operation fell to Kellingley Colliery, in North Yorkshire.

Known as the 'Big K', it just managed to reach its golden jubilee before the axe fell on December 18, 2015.

When the last miners came up from the last shift, they posed for the national media's cameras laughing and joking – but the bravado was skin-deep only; a few minutes later, some of the men were seen to be in tears.

Kellingley had been Britain's first TWO-million tonne colliery, which was one of the reasons for its longevity. Its five-year deal with nearby Drax power station ran out at the end of 2015 and was not renewed due to cheaper coal prices abroad. Drax continues to burn four million tonnes a year in three of its six boilers (the others burn biomass), but today the coal supplies come from the USA and Columbia.

"How can it be right that it's cheaper to transport coal half way round the world – past the gates of this very mine – to a power station that can be seen from here with the naked eye?" asked one of the miners as he came to the surface for the last time. "It's a disgrace... the country has thrown away an entire industry."

Kellingley was one of the country's newer collieries, being opened in 1965 after seven years of construction. A modern, fully mechanised deep mine with shafts driven down to 2,500ft, its output was about twice that of the old collieries west of Pontefract and its men were considered by the NCB to be 'technicians' rather than miners.

As more and more mines were shut down, it attracted displaced colliers from all over the country and had so many

former Scottish miners that it had a pipe band instead of a traditional brass band. Its success helped inspire the opening-up of the nearby Selby coalfield in the 1970s.

Although its faces were seven miles from the shafts by the end, the mine still had 30million tonnes of reserves – enough to keep it open for 15 more years – but the Government refused financial aid to owners UK Coal and instead agreed to subsidise a 'managed closure', throwing the 450-strong workforce on the scrapheap.

The day after the Kellingley closure, the miners and their families marched through the streets of nearby Knottingley. Thousands turned out and NUM branch officer Keith Poulson described it as "a celebration of the working lives we have shared together".

Kellingley was a superpit. Its winding gear was enclosed in metal cladding, and nobody passing its gates on the Knottingley-Goole road would have noticed that its wheels had stopped spinning, as they would have done at

the nation's penultimate deep mine, Thoresby, in Nottinghamshire.

The triple-decker cage at Kellingley hurtled miners half a mile into the bowels of the earth at 23ft a second. They then caught a train for a six-mile, 45-minute journey before spending the last 10 minutes lying on a mile-long conveyor belt travelling at 9ft a second. On that, they would be spaced out at 23ft intervals for safety reasons. Once at the face, they worked for 10 hours in 94F heat and 98% humidity.

Millions of pounds worth of cutters, conveyors, power supports, trains, ventilators and myriad other pieces of expensive and sophisticated equipment have been abandoned down there. There is no longer any other British deep mine to transfer them to (although the proposed Crofton drift mine has taken a mining machine). The shafts have been capped and the site is to be redeveloped by UK Coal's property division, Harworth Estates.

The very last piece of coal was symbolically brought to the surface on December 18 by miner Kevin McDonagh and the last tonne of coal was due to be put on display at the National Museum of Mining at Caphouse Colliery, near Wakefield, as a lasting reminder.

Also hopefully going to the museum will be a memorial that has stood outside the office entrance for many years, bearing the names of 17 men who lost their lives at Kellingley in its half-century of operation. ●

ABOVE: Although the last train to leave the operational colliery had run on December 18, services continued for a further six days to remove the stockpile and the curtain finally came down on Christmas Eve when No. 66118, carrying a 'last train' headboard to mark the occasion, departed for Drax power station. GORDON EDGAR **BELOW:** The very last shift at the very last deep mine, December 18, 2015. PRESS ASSOCIATION

DESTRUCTION
OF AN INDUSTRY

ABOVE: A sight guaranteed to generate mixed emotions among miners and those who depended on them for a living. A few people who worked in the pits were glad to see them go, but the vast majority of mineworkers feel tremendous sadness at the way their industry has been systematically destroyed over the last three or four decades. This symbolic photograph was taken at Calverton Colliery, Nottinghamshire, in January 2000 but could just as easily have been at any one of the hundreds of deep mines demolished with almost indecent haste in recent years. ROBIN STEWART-SMITH

IT is difficult to comprehend how quickly and extensively almost all signs of the vast colliery complexes have been swept away in Britain through demolition and redevelopment. Daw Mill, for instance, was closed in 2013 and had been unceremoniously wiped off the face of the earth within a matter of months.

That mine's abandonment was brought about by an underground fire but there have been numerous other reasons for closure over the years. These include geological faults, exhaustion of coal reserves, decline in demand, roof falls, floods and mergers of neighbouring mines, in which the haulage roads are linked underground and one set of surface buildings are taken out of use.

Decommissioning a mine involves more than demolishing the headstocks and the surface buildings; underground waterways have to be protected from future flooding that might occur once the shafts and roadways begin to deteriorate and the shafts have to be filled and capped.

The usual way of sealing off a mine is to remove all the ropes and pipes from inside the shaft, drill large holes through the wall into the strata at the bottom and then pipe in concrete to form an anchored seal. Thousands of tons of roadstone or rubble are then poured on top of that and finally the shaft is capped at the top with more concrete.

Deterioration starts quickly once the fans, pumps and power are turned off. Depending on the type of geology, a mine can quickly fill with water and its roadway roofs and sides can begin to collapse as the forces of nature take their course. Millions of pounds' worth of mining machinery and railway equipment is abandoned underground and left to its fate as there is no use for it elsewhere.

It's highly controversial when it is considered how much work and money went into sinking and establishing the ▶

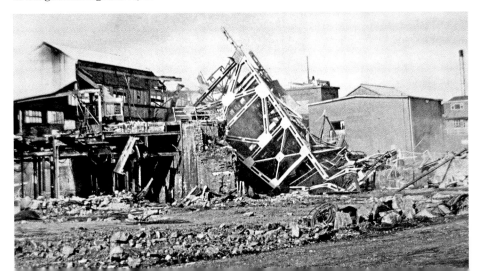

LEFT: A steel girder headstock comes crashing down in a mass of twisted metal at Victoria Colliery, Biddulph.

Britain's last **all-new** deep mine

IN the 1970s, the research teams of the National Coal Board were looking at several areas in which to expand once the older pits west of the Pennines and in Scotland had become exhausted. The new regions included a famous East Midlands beauty spot – the Vale of Belvoir, south-west of Grantham, beneath which lie at least half a billion tonnes of coal.

Three new superpits were planned on the outer edges of the vale – in the villages of Saltby, Hose and Asfordby – and would be served by railways operating on the Merry-go-Round system, taking coal to Trent valley power stations. Production was predicted to last about 75 years and provide employment for thousands of miners.

Fierce local opposition – not least from the Duke of Rutland, whose stately home, Belvoir Castle, towered over the vale – forced the longest and most expensive coal planning inquiry ever held in Britain. In the end, British Coal was allowed to go ahead with only one of the collieries, Asfordby, west of Melton Mowbray.

One of the reasons for that decision was that it lay in a locality already used for heavy industry (Holwell ironworks), whereas the other two would have been built in unspoilt rural areas. Being adjacent to British Rail's Old Dalby test track, Asfordby also required the shortest rail connection of the three. One school of thought is that it was sunk with the intention of one day being linked underground with Cotgrave Colliery.

The Asfordby shafts were sunk in 1986 but it was to be the mid-1990s before coal came fully on stream due to the area being bedevilled by more serious geological faults than British Coal had bargained for. Apart from this, the coal turned out to be the wrong quality and had to be taken to Rufford, near Mansfield, for blending with other coals before it could be marketed – a process known as 'sweeting'.

Asfordby thus turned out to be a 'white elephant'... the British coal industry's ill-fated final fling. It was closed in 1997 after barely a decade of its predicted three-quarters of a century. The virtually new Koepe winding towers were demolished by explosives in 1998 and some of the larger ancillary buildings have since been converted into a test centre for Britain's new generation of express passenger trains.

BELOW: Countdown to destruction. These three photographs show the demolition of the two winding towers at Asfordby Colliery in March 1998. A warning siren, a series of explosions, a sickening thud, a cloud of dust... then silence. PICTURES: NICK PIGOTT

ABOVE: 'Women against pit closures!' Doing their best to stave off the inevitable, the wives, mothers and daughters of Rufford men established a camp outside the colliery in 1993.

mines in the first place and when it's realised that the capping is as good as permanent – for even if a future generation decided to reopen the mines in the event of a global oil crisis or similar, lack of maintenance coupled with geological pressures will have made that impractical.

In reality, it would be quicker and more sensible to sink all-new shafts or drifts closer to the points the coalface had reached when the mines closed, which could be several miles from the old colliery pitheads. But the cost of sinking shafts and opening a new deep mine would be a billion pounds, according to UK Coal figures in 2009, and it could take anything up to seven years before it was able to produce any coal. In that time, a war could have been fought and lost.

Unlike in 1939 and 1973, Britain would have nothing to fall back on – and to rub salt into the wound, it was reported in late 2015 that the developers of a new potash mine in North Yorkshire have had to turn to foreign experts to sink their shafts because British engineers have lost the knowledge!

Mothballing of the nation's last three deep collieries might have been an option, but even long-term mothballing would require Government aid as it means not only maintaining the integrity of the infrastructure but keeping the underground ventilation and pumps in continuous operation. Harworth mine in Nottinghamshire was mothballed for a while and reportedly required a team of 100 men simply to keep it ticking over.

At Daw Mill, the underground blaze that had forced its closure in 2013 meant that a different procedure had to be undertaken as the mine had been evacuated as soon as the fire broke out and it had not been safe for anyone to re-enter since. As a result, demolition contractors had to devise a strategy whereby all the work to seal the shafts and an inclined drift was undertaken from the surface.

Bespoke shaft covers formed of four huge steel girders had to be designed specially. Once they had been fitted, it was possible to fill the shafts and then dismantle the headstocks in a controlled manner. ●

Then and **Now**

THE great majority of disused collieries in Britain have been demolished, especially those closed during the last two or three decades as a result of the modern emphasis on redeveloping and recycling. A few closed 40 or more years ago have had their surface buildings adapted for new uses but most sites have been redeveloped for a wide variety of purposes:
• The site of Wearmouth Colliery is now occupied by Sunderland FC's 48,000-capacity Stadium of Light plus an Olympic-sized swimming pool.
• Cortonwood, one of the flashpoints of the 1984/85 strike, is now one of numerous sites that have been turned into retail parks or supermarkets, as has Hucknall (see above/right).
• Ashington, which still had rows and rows of Victorian-style wooden-bodied wagons in its sidings as recently as the late 1980s, is an upmarket business park complete with fountains and flower beds.
• Shirebrook's site hosts the headquarters of a major sportswear company.
• Cotgrave is one of numerous sites that have been turned into housing estates.
• Other uses for old colliery locations include retail parks, leisure centres, warehouses, fast-food outlets and other service or leisure concerns – in fact, anything it seems but wealth-producing *manufacturing* industry.

Even people with a trained eye would be hard pressed these days to know they were passing a former colliery if they weren't familiar with the area.

Numerous spoil heaps have been levelled or landscaped and turned into country parks or golf courses and there is even a proposal to string a zip-wire between the headstocks of Clipstone Colliery (preserved as the tallest of their kind in Europe) and operate it as part of an adventure leisure attraction.

ABOVE: A stark demonstration of how Britain has changed in recent years: The top image shows Hucknall Colliery in full production on May 4, 1979, with a Class 56 propelling coal hoppers under the rapid loader as two Class 20s pass on the Nottingham-Worksop line. The bottom photograph – taken from the exact same location – reveals one of the most commonplace sights in modern Britain... a supermarket, car park and housing estate. The land in the foreground is now a station on the **Robin Hood Line.** PICTURES A KAYE AND R STEWART-SMITH

ABOVE: The imposing bulk of Shirebrook Colliery in August 1988. This site is now occupied by a national sports goods distribution centre. ROBIN STEWART-SMITH

WHERE TO SEE
COLLIERIES TODAY

A S if the closure of Britain's last three operational deep mines in 2015 was not bad enough, the country also lost two of its supposedly preserved collieries in the same period.

Snibston Colliery, in Leicestershire, closed on July 31 and Cumbria's Haig Colliery closed its doors at the end of the year.

Both had been fully open to the public with associated museums and what is particularly regrettable with regard to Snibston is that it was substantially complete with both headstocks and most of its outbuildings intact, whereas many preserved mines have only the winding house and headstocks left (and even then perhaps only one tower). Snibston also had an operational standard gauge railway on which passengers could travel.

It was closed as a cost-cutting measure by Leicestershire County Council, which controversially demolished the award-winning and relatively new 'Discovery' museum alongside it in early 2016 to make way for housing. The mine buildings themselves are listed as structures of architectural merit and will hopefully reopen one day on a limited scale.

The closures leave only half a dozen or so deep mine museums to continue trying to educate the next generation of children about one of Britain's greatest industries.

ABOVE: Lewis Merthyr Colliery, in the Rhondda Valley, is one of the best-kept mines in the UK and offers a simulated underground experience. NICK PIGOTT

THE FULL LIST OF SURVIVING LOCATIONS I

COLLIERIES OPEN TO THE PUBLIC:
Those towards the end of the list tend to have only the headstocks and winding houses left in situ. The first two in the list offer underground tours: note that some of the museums are open only on limited occasions and it is advisable to check before visiting.

CAPHOUSE
(The National Mining Museum for England)
Overton, near Wakefield, West Yorkshire
WF4 4RH
www.ncm.org.uk Tel: 01924 448806
Number of winding towers: 1
(plus 1 at Hope Pit on the same site)

BLAENAFON ('BIG PIT')
(Welsh National Coal Museum)
Blaenafon World Heritage Site, Torfaen
NP4 9XP
www.museumwales.ac.uk/en/bigpit
Tel: 029 2057 3650
Number of winding towers: 1

LADY VICTORIA
(Scottish National Mining Museum)
Newtongrange, Midlothian EH22 4QN
www.scottishminingmuseum.com
Tel: 0131 663 7519
Number of winding towers: 1

LEWIS MERTHYR
Rhondda Heritage Park, Trehafod CF37 2NP.
www.tourism.rctcbc.gov.uk
Tel: 01443 682036
Number of winding towers: 2

WOODHORN
QEII Country Park, near Ashington
NE63 9YF.
www.experiencewoodhorn.com
Tel: 01670 624455.
Number of winding towers: 2

PLEASLEY
Pit Lane, Pleasley, Nottinghamshire
NG19 7PH.
www.pleasleypittrust.org.uk
Number of winding towers: 2

CHATTERLEY WHITFIELD *
Chell, near Stoke-on-Trent, Staffordshire
ST6 8UW
Number of winding towers: 4
(* open only rarely, by prior appointment.
www.chatterleywhitfieldfriends.org.uk).

ASTLEY GREEN
Astley Green, Tyldesley, Manchester
M29 7JB
www.agcm.org.uk
Number of winding towers: 1

CEFN COED
Neath Road, Creunant, South Wales
SA10 8SN.
www.npt.gov.uk/
Number of winding towers: 2

BESTWOOD
Park Road, Bestwood, Nottinghamshire
NG6 8TQ
www.nottinghamshire.gov.uk/
Number of winding towers: 1

BEAMISH
Living Museum of the North, Beamish, County
Durham DH9 0RG www.beamish.org
Number of winding towers: 1
NB. The winding tower (the only surviving one with a vertical-cylinder steam engine) was relocated from nearby Beamish Second Colliery but the Mahogany drift mine (which is open to the public) is in its original position.

WASHINGTON 'F' PIT
Washington, County Durham NE37 1BJ
www.seeitdoitsunderland.co.uk/washington-f-pit
Number of winding towers: 1

BERSHAM
Rhostyllen, near Wrexham, North Wales.
Number of winding towers: 1
(Open on limited Sundays)

HOPEWELL
Cannop Hill, Speech House Rd, Coleford,
Gloucestershire GL16 7EL.
www.hopewellcolliery.com
Note: This is a drift mine and although underground tours are offered to the public, the large half-winding wheel and wooden replica headstock on the surface are for display purposes only.

COLLIERIES NOT NORMALLY OPEN TO THE PUBLIC:
(The first four on the list are substantially complete, the rest tend to comprise headgear and winding houses only.)

KELLINGLEY
Kellingley, North Yorkshire.
Number of winding towers: 2

Partial demolition of miscellaneous surface structures has taken place on most surviving heritage sites, with washeries and screens having been the biggest victims. Although there are a handful of coal preparation plants on opencast operations, the only traditional-style washery buildings today are replicas or re-sited examples.

The latest addition to the ranks of preserved headstocks and winding houses are those of Hatfield Colliery, near Doncaster, which Historic England saved from demolition in November 2015 with 48 hours to spare, but the office block and several other surrounding buildings have already been demolished.

Beamish has the only example of a working vertical-cylinder winding engine. This was moved from the nearby Beamish Second Colliery but the adjacent 'Mahogany' drift mine is in its original location.

Although several museums have realistic simulated coalface displays (some beneath the surface) only two deep coal mines (Caphouse and Blaenafon) offer genuine underground tours using original shafts. The public can also experience subterranean tours at several places including Beamish and the small Hopewell drift mine in the Forest of Dean. ●

ABOVE: By far the most complete coal mine still standing in Britain in terms of surviving buildings and headstocks is the disused Chatterley Whitfield Colliery in Staffordshire – now unique as the only one possessing four winding towers. In the 1990s, it was open to the public and operated underground tours, but the workings then flooded, the public visits were heavily restricted and the site has since become increasingly run-down and overgrown. It is, however, a national treasure and should be given the restoration and tender loving care it deserves.

ABOVE LEFT: A new experience: Three-year-old George Reeves, of Leicester, sees coal for the first time in his life during a visit to the Great Central Railway in 2015. Back in 1992, the GCR purchased a set of 16-ton coal wagons following an initiative launched by the author of this bookazine and now runs them at galas and other special events.
ABOVE RIGHT: How children learn about the past. A group of excited youngsters prepare to go underground at the Welsh National Mining Museum in Blaenafon.

PRING 2016 IS AS FOLLOWS:

THORESBY
Edwinstowe, Nottinghamshire.
Number of winding towers: 2

SNIBSTON
Coalville, Leicestershire.
Number of winding towers: 3 (2 + 1)

CASTLEBRIDGE
Clackmannanshire, Scotland
Number of winding towers: 1

HATFIELD
Stainforth, South Yorkshire.
Number of winding towers: 2

CLIPSTONE
Clipstone, Nottinghamshire.
Number of winding towers: 2

PENALLTA
Near Ystrad Mynach, South Wales
Number of winding towers: 2

BARNSLEY MAIN
Stairfoot, near Barnsley, South Yorkshire.
Number of winding towers: 1

HAIG
Kells, Whitehaven, Cumbria.
Number of winding towers: 1

TOWER
Near Hirwaun, South Wales.
Number of winding towers: 1

HETTY
Hopkinstown, near Pontypridd, South Wales.
Number of winding towers: 1

Large winding towers standing on their own without a winding house can also be found at the former collieries of Frances (Fife), Mary (Fife), Barony (Ayrshire) and Grange (Shropshire), and there are numerous former coal sites in the UK possessing small wooden or replica headstocks, some authentic, some replicas. Perhaps the strangest one of all was an 1879 wooden headstock erected over a mineshaft sunk by the late steeplejack and demolition contractor Fred Dibnah in his Lancashire garden.

The earlier a mine closed, the more likely it is to have survived reasonably intact, New Haden (shut in 1943) being an example, but such remnants are usually on private land. There are headstocks belonging to mines or former mines producing gold, tin, haematite, potash or other minerals, and some (such as Florence mine in Cumbria) have winding towers that make them look like collieries, but those are not part of this survey. There are also two currently non-operational anthracite drift mines in South Wales, at Cwmgrach and Aberpergwm.

OTHER COAL-ASSOCIATED MUSEUM OR HERITAGE SITES INCLUDE:
Black Country Living Museum, Dudley (West Midlands)*; Blists Hill Museum (Shropshire); Bilsthorpe Mining Museum, Bilsthorpe (Nottinghamshire); Durham Mining Museum, Spennymoor (Co Durham); South Wales Miners Museum, Afan Forest Park, near Port Talbot, South Wales; Elsecar Heritage Centre, Elsecar (South Yorkshire); National Gas Museum, Aylestone Rd, Leicester; Kidwelly Industrial Museum, Kidwelly (Carmarthenshire); Fred Dibnah Heritage Centre, Bolton, Lancashire; Foxfield Colliery (Staffordshire), which has two winding towers and is associated with the Foxfield Steam Railway. There are also a number of small open restoration sites, such as the site of Califat Colliery, near Swannington in Leicestershire, but surviving surface buildings at the nearby Calcutta and Moira collieries are among several in Britain that are now in private hands as commercial premises or dwelling houses.
* There is public access into a small drift mine at this location.

SOCIETIES AND FORUMS: Finally, there are a large number of societies and web-based forums specialising in coal-mining history and ones that can be highly recommended for further and much more detailed information than can be contained in a general publication such as this, are the Northern Mine Research Society (www.nmrs.org.uk), the Industrial Railway Society (www.irsociety.co.uk), Subterranea Britannica (www.subbrit.org.uk) and Healey Hero (www.healeyhero.co.uk).

SAFETY FIRST...
Disused mine sites can be very dangerous places. Never enter them without permission – and never throw anything down a hole or remove a ladder or rope. There could be someone underground!

'IF THE LIGHTS GO OUT, DON'T BLAME US!'

THE words on the headline above were written on hundreds of banners and badges carried during a march to mark the closure of Britain's last deep mine, Kellingley Colliery, just before Christmas 2015.

They refer to the British Government's energy policy, which many people claim is no longer secure or self-sufficient.

The workforces at Kellingley and other collieries had an understandable right to feel bitter and angry at being thrown on the scrapheap because the UK's energy policy for at least the next few years still requires 20% of the nation's needs to be met by the burning of coal – and much of that coal is now being shipped thousands of miles from the other side of the world.

It is being imported even though the UK still possesses millions of tons itself and to make matters even more bizarre, it's being moved hundreds of miles once it gets here… by trains from ports to power stations that are themselves sitting on or near a coalfield!

The term 'economics of the madhouse' is often used by critics of British policies in this regard and is brought to mind by the general secretary of the NUM, Chris Kitchen, who says: "If the gas supply is ever turned off, we've had it. People say mining was a dirty dangerous job and good riddance… but has the nation made a mistake in closing it all down? We've left ourselves no options if we need to change our mind."

One would expect an NUM stalwart to feel that way, of course, but anxieties are also felt by senior Conservative politician Lord Howell who, speaking only a few months after one of Britain's foreign-owned power stations had come within a whisker of having to ration electricity recently, warned that the UK's energy policy is not sufficiently long-term or robust and leaves perilously little margin for error.

The nation's last collieries were closed because coal prices nose-dived and they were no longer profitable, yet the critics make the valid point that, historically, coal prices have always fallen and risen and that as recently as 2004 to 2008 they rocketed by 100%-plus. When, as will almost certainly happen eventually, they shoot up again, Britain will be unable to capitalise as it no longer has any mothballed mines left to reopen.

As one soon-to-be-redundant miner put it in 2015: "I can't believe we're being asked to leave such a great natural resource under the ground without any means of getting back into it if circumstances change."

At the moment, there is very little in the way of a contingency policy and Coalfields Communities Campaign chairman Bill Flanagan is on record as saying: "Britain could find itself in a hostage position in the future."

It is understood that such a scenario was foreseen by Margaret Thatcher's Government in the 1980s but that it took the view that if one or two nations did cut off supplies, there would always be another country somewhere in the world that would be happy to make up the shortfall. It was a gamble and remains so to this day.

Prior to the 1980s, coal reserves were thought of as a national asset and financial losses were tolerated as preferable to squandering the nation's hard currency on imports, but that way of thinking has long since been replaced by short-term financial expediency.

With North Sea oil and gas production having peaked, with geothermal and hydro-electric schemes not being prominent in the UK and with most biomass having to be imported, the only serious indigenous alternative to solar, wind, wave, nuclear and the burning of non-recyclable waste in the event of a global energy crisis would be opencast coal. Indeed, it has been said in defence of pit closures that if ever Britain needed its own coal again in a hurry, it would simply 'go into the side of a mountain'. However, most opencast coal is not of the highest quality as it's not deep enough.

In the years when the UK was largely self-sufficient in energy terms, few could have imagined that such a

ABOVE: Coal-fired power stations such as Didcot have been closed at a rapid rate. During the station's heyday in 1987, Class 56 No. 56020 leaves the cooling towers of the Oxfordshire plant behind to collect another trainload of coal from the then-extensive British colliery network.
RAIL PHOTOPRINTS

ABOVE: A sign of changing times: A wind turbine within sight of Kellingley coal mine (right) and Eggborough coal-fired power station (left). NICK PIGOTT

The UK's remaining coal-fired power stations

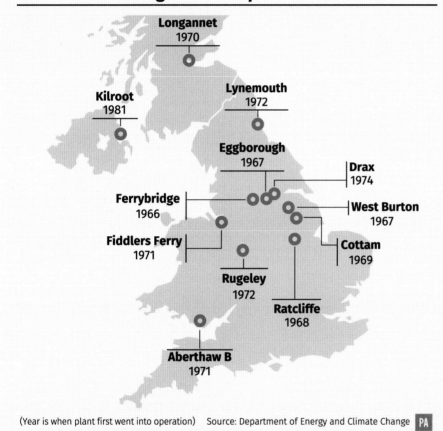

Longannet
1970

Kilroot
1981

Lynemouth
1972

Eggborough
1967

Drax
1974

Ferrybridge
1966

West Burton
1967

Fiddlers Ferry
1971

Cottam
1969

Rugeley
1972

Ratcliffe
1968

Aberthaw B
1971

(Year is when plant first went into operation)   Source: Department of Energy and Climate Change   PA

ABOVE: When this map was produced by the Department of Energy & Climate Change shortly after the closure of Ironbridge power station in 2015, Britain still had a dozen coal-fired stations left, but since then Ferrybridge has shut down, the closures of Rugeley, Eggborough and Longannet have been announced, 75% of Fiddlers Ferry is to close and the others are likely to switch to the burning of biomass with 50% of Drax having already done so. Yet, perversely, Germany opened an all-new coal-burning power station only two years ago.

'Clean Coal Technology'

WHAT is especially galling for many ex-miners is the fact that 'lean-burn' and carbon-capture systems exist and have done for several years.

'Clean coal' isn't simply an oxymoron; it exists in several different ways, one being the use of 'scrubbing' (desulphurisation) units that can filter out up to 95% of the pollutants before they reach the atmosphere. Carbon dioxide, one of the greatest contributors to global warming, can be captured either before or after combustion of coal, depending on the method used.

Back in the days when British Coal was in existence, the company spent millions of pounds researching clean-burn technology at its laboratories near Cheltenham and Burton-upon-Trent. The project was abandoned when British Coal was split up for privatisation, but work to reduce 'greenhouse gases' continued in other parts of the world and has reached such a stage of advancement that there is no real need for coal to be considered 'dirty' in environmental terms any longer.

Desulphurisation equipment is now installed in most western power stations and means that 95% of sulphur and nitrogen is filtered out before it can escape into the atmosphere to cause 'acid rain'.

Precipitators can remove 90% of fly ash residue, while gasification plants can convert coal into gas to make another form of 'clean coal'. Gasification, as the name suggests, is a way of producing gas from coal rather than burning the solid and is an updated version of the traditional process that used to produce coal gas (sometimes known as town gas), used for heating and municipal lighting in the days before industrial-scale production of natural gas.

Coupled with carbon dioxide separation and carbon-capture-and-storage facilities, these developments mean there could be a future for coal in an environmentally conscious world after all.

For British deep miners, it's all too little, too late.

---

situation would ever be allowed to come to pass, but the harsh reality is that in a market-led economy, privately owned deep-mining companies have simply been unable to compete with cheap imported coal from the likes of Columbia and Russia even when the price of transporting it round the world is factored in. Imposition of an increased UK carbon tax was the straw that broke the camel's back.

American coal has also been flooding onto the international market as a result of extensive fracking there (the controversial method of releasing shale gas from underground rocks by fracturing them with high-pressure water) and that, coupled with dumping of cheap coal on the international market from the weakening Chinese economy, has skewed the energy business.

In Britain, hope is being placed by some people on fracking too, but shale gas is - like coal - a fossil fuel and there are many people on whom

that particular irony appears to have been lost.

Just 24 hours before Kellingley closed in December 2015, the Government awarded more than 100 exploration licences allowing fracking beneath national parks and areas of outstanding natural beauty, including the North Yorkshire Moors, Exmoor, the Peak District and the Lincolnshire Wolds.

Although the record on mine safety and under-age labour in some third-world countries is extremely poor, ▶

particularly in parts of South America and the Indian sub-continent, the combination of a strong pound and a historically low global price has finished off what the Government started after the 1984/85 miners' strike.

As recently as 1992 – seven years after the strike ended – young mining recruits were being told by British Coal that they had "a job for life", but those promises came crashing down on the black day of October 13 that year when Government Minister Michael Heseltine announced that three-quarters of the remaining British coal industry was to be shut down and that 39,000 miners at 31 pits were to be added to the country's dole queues.

In those days, it was the 'dash for gas' by electricity generators that was conveniently blamed. A quarter of a century later, it is 'environmental and carbon emission targets' – yet closing the mines that survived the 1992 cull has failed to eliminate Britain's carbon emissions and despite the reduction in the number of coal-fired power stations, the nation is still buying and burning imported coal, prompting the question "What difference does it make to the environment whether it's imported or not?"

That is a question Government ministers would rather not answer, for it is related not so much to environmental quotas but to market forces.

The way things are going, there could soon be no British plants capable of burning coal anyway. Didcot, Ironbridge and Ferrybridge power stations have all closed recently and Rugeley (even though it has a flue gas desulphurisation plant) is due to shut in summer 2016.

ABOVE LEFT: 'If the lights go out, don't blame us'. This was the stark message being sent loud and clear to the Government by those who joined a mass demonstration through the streets of Knottingley on December 19, 2015 following the closure of nearby Kellingley Colliery. How his generation will judge the decisions of the early 21st century, only time will tell.
ABOVE RIGHT: If only they'd known... an NCB poster of the 1970s.

Among those that are left, Drax has switched half its boilers to burn imported biomass. This despite the fact that all-new lignite coal burning power stations are still being opened in Germany! Third World countries too are building them, adding weight to the many people who believe Britain has allowed its mining industry to die prematurely.

At least there's plenty of good quality coal left if future generations ever did need to find a way of reversing the situation, for in the 1980s, British Coal sank 950 boreholes to establish how much still existed under our feet and off our coasts. The results were

astonishing – no less than 1.2billion tons. Even if environmental pressures are still relevant many years from now, 'clean coal', carbon capture and gasification technologies are likely to have improved so much by then that mining those reserves could once again become acceptable.

In the meantime, wind turbines and solar farms are springing up like mushrooms all over Britain, some on the site of old collieries, yet such renewable energy sources are unreliable. They are affected by the wrong kind of weather (turbines don't generate any energy at all if they're not turning) and even biomass supplies are at the mercy of international shipping delays and cannot be stockpiled for more than a few days due to the risk of damp. New nuclear power stations to replace those reaching the end of their lives haven't been built yet, leaving the UK as a net importer of energy and therefore at the mercy of foreign instability.

No-one would try to argue that a carbon-free world based totally on renewable energy is not a laudable long-term aim... but was it really necessary for an industry that had served the country so well for so long to be destroyed quite so brutally in the process?

Back in the 1970s, the NCB ran a national poster campaign proclaiming 'People will always need coal'.

If only they'd had a crystal ball. ●

The last big player left on **the Coalfield**

THE Coal Authority owns, on behalf of the nation, the majority of the vast coal reserves in Britain and licenses what little is left in terms of current mining operations – mainly opencast.

It also supervises decommissioning and shaft-capping of closed collieries and manages the effects of past mining, including any subsidence damage claims that are not the responsibility of licensed operators. Mine water pollution and other legacy issues come within its brief too.

Most of its 170 members of staff are based at its headquarters in Mansfield, Nottinghamshire, but the authority has regional engineers based in other coalfield areas so that it can respond quickly to safety issues wherever they occur.

Communicating with members of the public is one of its priorities and in this respect, it has a heritage centre containing historic underground plans for the thousands of collieries Britain once possessed. In some cases, a single colliery might have had several hundred plans over the course of its 100-years-plus lifetime, so the collection is extensive and pinpoints the exact locations of underground roadways, shaft and drift entries.

BELOW: A long line of wind turbines photographed from the former Hatfield Colliery in Yorkshire.